BIOLOGICAL STATISTICS:

AN INTRODUCTION

McGRAW-HILL SERIES IN
PROBABILITY AND STATISTICS

DAVID BLACKWELL AND HERBERT SOLOMON, Consulting Editors

Bharucha-Reid Elements of the Theory of Markov Processes and
   Their Applications
Dubins and Savage How to Gamble If You Must
Ehrenfeld and Littauer Introduction to Statistical Methods
Li Introduction to Experimental Methods
Graybill Introduction to Linear Statistical Models, Volume I
Mood and Graybill Introduction to the Theory of Statistics
Pearce Biological Statistics: An Introduction
Wadsworth and Bryan Introduction to Probability and
   Random Variables
Weiss Statistical Decision Theory
Wolf Elements of Probability and Statistics

BIOLOGICAL STATISTICS:

AN INTRODUCTION

S. C. PEARCE

Head of Statistics Section
East Malling Research Station
Maidstone, Kent, England

McGraw-Hill Book Company

New York, St. Louis, San Francisco,
Toronto, London, Sydney

PREFACE

For the last twenty-six years I have been a mathematician working among biologists, and I have continually been made aware how much each has to learn from the other in the conduct of experiments. Time and again I have explained to a colleague what I was doing, but he has not understood. When I explained further, until at last comprehension dawned, the biologist often restated what I meant in words that were very different but often much clearer. Mathematical concepts are precise, but they must be applied and clothed with reality before they are useful; biological concepts are more subtle, but sometimes too vague for experimental verification. An amalgam of the two can have qualities possessed by neither alone.

The same thought has come to me while lecturing to biologists. Sometimes a student has interrupted, anxious to assure himself that he has understood correctly. Often his interpretation of my remark was couched in language more apt than my mathematical jargon, and I have been grateful for it. Indeed many of the phrases in this book were given to me by some biologist trying to get things straight.

Over the years I have come to explain statistical ideas in a less mathematical way, basing my explanations on an analysis of experiments rather than on the calculus of probabilities. This has prompted many biologists to ask me to recommend a reference book on the subject, but I have had to explain that no book deals with the subject from quite this angle. The present text is intended to overcome this deficiency.

This book contains only a little mathematics. I have tried to discuss experimental situations of all kinds and to classify them according to what the experimenter knows and what he is trying to find out. For each class of situation, I have been content to state the techniques appropriate to it without proof, assuming that my reader will not really care how they were derived so long as it is clear when they could be used. This book is, in fact, more a study of scientific method than of statistical fundamentals.

The book is addressed primarily to the biologist who wishes to apply statistical techniques in his research and who either knows nothing about them or has attended a course that he found difficult. It begins at the beginning. Although it is not comprehensive, it covers the main ideas of the measurement of variation, the analysis of variance, correlation and regres-

sion, the analysis of covariance, and a simple multivariate approach. With
these ideas the reader should be able to proceed to more advanced texts.

I have not devised the text for use in the classroom, though I have had
in mind the statistics course where a mathematician has undertaken, perhaps a little against his will, to teach some statistics to a class of biologists,
who for their part are perhaps rather reluctant also. I think that this book
could be helpful as parallel reading.

The examples have been chosen from a range of biological studies, and
I am grateful to those who supplied them. However, when it came to
explaining someone else's experiment, I often felt inadequate, and sub-
stituted an example of my own. I am sorry about this, but in a book of this
kind it is not enough to describe how the technique was used if one cannot
explain the reason why. I hope that the apparent emphasis on fruit trees
will not be irksome; the methods are of much wider application.

Acknowledgments

I am much indebted for data to Dr. F. R. Tubbs, Director of the East
Malling Research Station, and also to the members of the staff directly
involved, namely, Mr. R. J. Garner (Chapter 1), Mr. A. P. Preston
(Section 2.6), Mr. D. H. Maggs (Table 6.6), Dr. J. E. Crosse (Table 6.17),
and Miss E. M. Glenn (Table 10.3). The apple data used in Chapter 12
were obtained from the Record Office of the research station.

Others who helped with data are:

Mr. P. H. Brown and officers of the National Agricultural Advisory
Service for the data in Table 6.13.

Mr. J. O. Green of the Grassland Research Institute, Hurley, Berk-
shire, England, for the data in Tables 3.8, 8.2, and 8.7.

Mrs. Howeler-Coy of the Division of Public Health, Hobart, Australia,
for the data in Table 2.2.

Dr. Janet Sprent of Goldsmith's College, London, for the data in
Tables 3.3 and 9.1.

I am also indebted to Professors W. G. Cochran and M. S. Bartlett
and to the editor of the *Empire Journal of Experimental Agriculture* for
permission to use the data in Table 4.1.

I am grateful to Mr. P. Sprent and Dr. Janet Sprent for reading an
earlier text and making suggestions that led to its development in the present
form. I have been much helped by the comments of Dr. C. I. Bliss and Mr.
D. A. Holland.

I am indebted to the executors of the late Sir Ronald Fisher, F.R.S.,
formerly of Cambridge, to Dr. Frank Yates, F.R.S., Rothamsted, and to

Messrs. Oliver & Boyd Ltd., Edinburgh, for permission to reprint Tables III and V from the book "Statistical Tables for Biological, Agricultural and Medical Research."

I am also indebted to Professor E. S. Pearson and the trustees of "Biometrika" for permission to reprint parts of "New Statistical Table IV."

S. C. PEARCE

CONTENTS

Preface   v

CHAPTER 1. AT THE BEGINNING   **1**

*Reasons for experimenting, and the
measurement of variability.*

      1.1   Some reasons for experimenting   2
      1.2   Statistical purposes of an experiment   4
      1.3   The individuality of experiments   5
      1.4   The measurement of variation   6
      1.5   Population and sample   8
      1.6   The addition of variation   10

CHAPTER 2. ESTIMATES AND TESTS WITH THE ANALYSIS OF
                 VARIANCE   13

*What an analysis of variance is for and how its
interpretation can be adapted to answer questions of
various kinds.*

      2.1   Description of the analysis of variance   14
      2.2   A calculated example   15
      2.3   Estimation procedures   16
      2.4   The F test and the idea of significance   19
      2.5   The t test in its two forms   21
      2.6   Multiple-range tests   24
      2.7   Sequential experiments   25

CHAPTER 3. ANALYSIS OF VARIANCE FOR ORTHOGONAL
                 DESIGNS   31

*The main classes of experimental designs. How they
enable accuracy to be improved while still permitting
the use of the analysis of variance.*

      3.1   Some definitions   32
      3.2   Orthogonal two-way classifications   34
      3.3   Orthogonal three-way classifications   40

ix

3.4   A numerical example of Latin square data   43
3.5   Graeco-Latin squares   46
3.6   Multiple Latin squares   47

CHAPTER 4.   AN EXAMINATION OF ASSUMPTIONS   49

*The assumptions implicit in the analysis of variance
and how they can often be met by "transforming" the data.
Such transformations are sometimes biologically meaningful
and can be a help in interpretation.*

4.1   Randomization   50
4.2   Replication   51
4.3   Homogeneity of error   52
4.4   Additivity   54
4.5   Discontinuity   56
4.6   Transformations   57
4.7   Statistical arguments for transformation   58
4.8   Presentation of results using transformations   60
4.9   The transformation of discontinuous variates   62
4.10 Hidden assumptions   64

CHAPTER 5.   ANALYSIS OF VARIANCE FOR AN ARBITRARY
             DESIGN   67

*Even if the designs of Chapter 3 have not been used, it
is often still possible to use the analysis of variance.*

5.1   Some basic ideas in the analysis of variance   68
5.2   A simple example of an analysis of variance for an
      unspecified design   70
5.3   Checking of computations and the evaluation of block
      parameters   74
5.4   Three-way nonorthogonal classifications   76
5.5   The uses of nonorthogonal designs   79
5.6   Randomization of nonorthogonal designs   80

CHAPTER 6.   ANALYSIS OF VARIANCE FOR SOME
             NONORTHOGONAL DESIGNS   81

*Some designs are described that lack the rigidity
of those in Chapter 3 but still have a fair amount of
organization. These facilitate experimentation in
restrictive conditions.*

6.1   Designs of type T 82
6.2   Numerical example of the analysis of data from a
        design of type T 85
6.3   Designs of type S 89
6.4   Numerical examples of the analysis of data from a
        design of type S 93
6.5   Designs of type G 97
6.6   Numerical example of the analysis of data from a
        design of type G 99

CHAPTER 7. MISSING DATA   105

*An experiment has been carefully designed and then
something goes wrong with the plans; it is shown that
much of the desired information can often be salvaged
from the wreck.*

7.1   The estimation of missing plot values   106
7.2   Effects of nonorthogonality in a defective orthogonal
        design   109
7.3   Other methods of dealing with defective data   110
7.4   Statistical tests for the rejection of plots   113
7.5   Rejection in difficult situations   114
7.6   Biological considerations   116

CHAPTER 8. PARTITIONS OF THE SUM OF SQUARED
            DEVIATIONS FOR TREATMENTS   119

*If the treatments are related to one another in a logical
scheme, the analysis of variance can often be taken a stage
further so as to answer more specific questions.*

8.1   Individual degrees of freedom   120
8.2   Partitioning with an orthogonal design with all
        treatments equally replicated   121
8.3   Partitioning in other circumstances   123
8.4   Linear, parabolic, and cubic effects   125
8.5   A numerical example   126
8.6   A factorial partition   128
8.7   More general factorial partitions   131
8.8   Split plots   133
8.9   The analysis of data from experiments with
        split plots   134
8.10 Some more complicated cases   138

CHAPTER 9.   INTERACTIONS AND CONFOUNDING   139

*The partitioning described in Chapter 8 has an especially
useful form in some instances. Also, sometimes it is
possible to sacrifice information of little interest to learn more
about matters of greater importance.*

9.1   Instances when interactions do not provide a
       suitable partition   140
9.2   A numerical example involving interactions   142
9.3   Some special cases   145
9.4   Confounding   147

CHAPTER 10.   CORRELATION AND REGRESSION   149

*So far variable quantities have been thought of in isolation,
but often one wants to learn how closely they are related and in
what way.*

10.1   Correlation coefficients   150
10.2   Conflicting correlations   153
10.3   Three variates   154
10.4   Surveys and experiments   158
10.5   Regression coefficients   160
10.6   The accuracy of estimation of regression
        lines   163
10.7   The comparison of regression coefficients   164
10.8   Partial regression   165
10.9   Curvilinear regression   166

CHAPTER 11.   THE ANALYSIS OF COVARIANCE   169

*Once methods are available for discerning how one quantity affects
another, it becomes possible to remove the effects of certain sources
of variation irrelevant to the experiment.*

11.1   The need to adjust one variate by another   170
11.2   Computations in the analysis of covariance   171
11.3   Uses of the analysis of covariance   174
11.4   Assumptions in the analysis of covariance   176

CHAPTER 12.   MULTIVARIATE METHODS   179

*A description of component analysis, which is useful for suggesting
how a number of observed quantities are being affected by a smaller
number of underlying stimuli.*

12.1   The resolution of conflicting correlations   180
12.2   A simple example of component analysis   182
12.3   A geometric interpretation   184
12.4   A more complicated example of component
          analysis   186
12.5   The interpretation of component analyses   189
12.6   Alternative systems of vectors   191
12.7   Factor analysis   193
12.8   Some practical considerations   194

SUGGESTIONS FOR FURTHER READING   197

APPENDIX I   CRITICAL VALUES OF t 201

APPENDIX II   CRITICAL VALUES OF F 203

Index   209

CHAPTER ONE

AT THE BEGINNING[1]

REASONS FOR EXPERIMENTING, AND THE
MEASUREMENT OF VARIABILITY.

[1] The reader is advised to have a copy of "Statistical Tables for Biological,
Agricultural and Medical Research" by Sir Ronald A. Fisher and Dr. F. Yates,
published by Oliver & Boyd Ltd., Edinburgh, 1949. These tables will be referred to
passim as "Fisher and Yates."

1.1   SOME REASONS FOR EXPERIMENTING

It is often said that the experimental approach is fundamental in all scientific
work, but such a statement needs examination. To most people an "experiment" is something they did at school or as students in order to learn
laboratory techniques and to confirm what they had been taught. Consequently no belief depended upon it. If the result was unexpected, it was
concluded that the technique had not been properly carried out; no one
decided that the corpus of scientific knowledge was ill-founded because
there was experimental evidence that contradicted it. In research, however,
until the experiment has been completed no one knows what the answer is.
There may be reasonable belief that the results ought to work out in a certain
way, but there must be some doubt or the experiment would never have been
initiated. Sometimes there are no grounds for any belief at all and the experiment is intended to find some. The experiment having been conducted,
belief may be greatly modified or confirmed. Before going any further it
will be as well to consider what role experimentation plays in research.

The classical purpose of an experiment is to establish the validity of a
way of thought. A scientist looks at the information already established and
thinks he sees a pattern. This enables him to foresee what would happen in
conditions not yet studied. He then discovers what does happen in such
circumstances. If he is proved to be right, he feels that he has reasons for
trusting his interpretation further; if things work out quite differently, he
must think again. For example, suppose that an anthropologist were interested in the distribution of blood groups. He might be inclined to believe that
the genes A and B, that is, those associated with clotting, must each have
arisen from a single mutation. He might then conclude that each would be

2

found with maximum frequency in one area and would become less common as one moved away, though he would have to allow for discrepancies brought about by migration of populations. He would investigate the matter to see how closely his conclusion agreed with the facts and would be quite encouraged by Professor Hogben's maps,[2] though the absence of gene B among American Indians would obviously cause him some difficulty.

The great examples of this approach, however, are to be found in the physical sciences. For example, Newton was aware of Kepler's laws of planetary motion that planets had been observed to move round the sun in elliptical orbits. By a brilliant piece of mathematics he argued that this would happen if there were a gravitational force between sun and planet that diminished with the square of increasing distance between them. This is the pattern, and falling apples fit into it no less than circling planets. Now Newton's mind began to work the other way. If this pattern is not just an amusing coincidence, there could be bodies moving round the sun in other second-degree curves—parabolas and hyperbolas as well as ellipses. How is it that only ellipses have been observed? It is here that the second flash of insight came. There are such orbits—those of some of the comets. Only one comet was needed to justify the whole train of thought, yet without it the whole of planetary theory would have been little more than a fascinating speculation.

It may be objected that Newton performed no experiment to justify his hypothesis, but this is because he was lucky. When Kekulé thought of the benzene ring, in order to confirm his ideas he had to set to work in the laboratory and demonstrate that there were in fact three different dinitro-benzenes. Again, Galton observed that dogs become attentive and prick up their ears even when nothing has been heard. He concluded that they must be able to hear sounds of a pitch higher than those audible to human beings, but he had to make specially shrill whistles to show that he was right. Certainly one reason for conducting experiments is to justify a line of reasoning. It is an immensely important one, because quite a small fact, itself of little importance, can justify a thought that embraces the universe.

Nevertheless, it would be a mistake to suppose that all experiments are so powerful. Sometimes there is no hypothesis at all. An agriculturist seeking to find an improved strain of wheat might make a number of similar crosses and then test them to find out which are of especial value. In such a trial there could be no question of asking which cross was expected to be best or whether the experiment had or had not confirmed current thought.

[2] Julian Huxley and A. C. Haddon, "We Europeans," pp. 130–131, Jonathan Cape, Ltd., London, 1935.

Indeed, if all the crosses were made with the same parents, as they might well be, there could be no reason for differentiating between them, yet a trial would be a thoroughly scientific procedure. Sometimes there are several hypotheses. Thus, in trying to standardize a method for determining the proportion of phosphate in plant tissues, an experimenter might vary temperature at different stages of the determination; he might try different rates of stirring and methods of filtering the precipitate. He would do this because he had a number of alternative hypotheses about the causes of variation in his results and he wished to discriminate between them to find the ones that could most profitably be studied further.

The list of possible purposes could be continued, but there is no need for this. Experiments are as diverse as people. There is, however, one thing that they all have in common. The word "experiment" is cognate with "experience," and every experiment is *an appeal to experience made by someone who has thought about the subject as far as his existing knowledge permits.* The element of thought is essential, because an experiment arises from a combination of knowing and not knowing. If enough were known, there would be no need for the experiment; if nothing were known, there would be nothing to indicate one experiment rather than another. Poised thus between knowing and not knowing, an experimenter must be very clear in his own mind where the boundary lies; only painstaking thought will help him to decide.

1.2   STATISTICAL PURPOSES OF AN EXPERIMENT

A statistician asked to set out possible reasons for an experiment would probably reply promptly that there were two, one to "test" and the other to "estimate." Asked to explain further, he would point out that there are two possible kinds of answers. One is the "Yes" or "No" sort that is appropriate to questions like: Is the average pulse rate of women different from that of men of the same age? Is the water content of oranges increased by irrigation? Finding the answers to such questions is called testing.

The other sort of question calls for a number as an answer, e.g., What is the average pulse rate of an adult? What is the mean water content of oranges? An experiment to answer such questions is said to be for purposes of estimation.

It is clear that the two operations are not completely different. To *test*, it is usually necessary to estimate two or more quantities to see if they are different. To *estimate*, it is first necessary to know how wide a generalization can be made. Nevertheless the distinction is an important one. Clearly an arithmetical process that provides the answer to the one kind of question will need modification before it will help with the other.

So far two classifications of experimental situations have been considered. One has concentrated on the number of hypotheses being studied, whether one, none, or several; the other, on whether the task is to test an assertion or to estimate a quantity. In fact, the two classifications are not entirely different. The classical experiment for testing a line of thought is intended to test in the statistician's sense also; this is so even though the estimation of a number or series of numbers is involved. Thus the purpose may be to find if the F_2 generation do indeed segregate in a $9:3:3:1$ ratio, and the question is whether the observed ratio is sufficiently different from the expected one to cast doubt on the assertion.

On the other hand, experiments in which there is no clear hypothesis may belong to either of the statistician's classes. Thus, in the trial of new strains of wheat, the purpose is to estimate the yield of each strain. It cannot be to test anything, because it is known that all the strains are genetically different from one another and yield is genetically determined in any specified environmental conditions. On the other hand, in the experiment on the standardization of a method of analysis there are several hypotheses and each needs testing.

1.3   THE INDIVIDUALITY OF EXPERIMENTS

As has already been said, experiments are very diverse in character, but no one can conduct a successful one unless he is clear about exactly what he wants to do. It is a great error, but one into which even great statisticians have fallen, to suppose that the correct way of analyzing a body of data depends solely on the form of the data. It depends only on the purpose of the experiment. The way in which the investigation has been carried out, and thus the data available, may preclude certain methods of analysis, but it can happen that one of those precluded is the one needed to answer the question under study. In that case the experiment has been so badly designed as to be worthless. Statistical techniques can be invaluable for determining the answers to given questions; they cannot decide the questions to be asked. These should arise from the experimenter's thought about the subject and from nothing else. A dozen people might collect the same data, but each for a different purpose; in that case each body of data would need to be analyzed differently. Thus, several experimenters might be studying the effect of wind speed and temperature on the migration of a certain species of insect. *A* knows that whenever a certain combination of these two factors occurs, the insects migrate, and he wants to find out if both factors are essential. *B* knows that they migrate when the wind speed falls below a critical value, and he wants to know if this value is affected by temperature. *C* is in the opposite position of knowing that they migrate above a critical temperature and he wishes to know if this value is affected by wind speed, while *D* is seeking factors conducive to migration and is studying these two separately and in conjunction as being the most likely he can think of. The point is that all might use the same apparatus and collect the same information, yet each would be carrying out a different experiment, so the method of statistical analysis that would answer the question of one would need to be modified before it could answer the question of another. Every experiment is dominated by its purpose, and techniques are always secondary.

A good statistician knows this, and he is therefore careful not to impose his own ideas of what needs to be done, but tries rather to draw out of the experimenter exactly what the latter thinks he knows already and what he wants to know. The experimenter's responsibility is to have thought hard in his own terms until he is ready for an appeal to experience to decide what cannot be found from existing knowledge and he is in a position to explain what the appeal is about. The statistician, for his part, should try to give quantitative form to what he is told so that he may test or estimate what is needed. Therefore the experimenter must lead the partnership. If he fails to do so, the statistician out of desperation may be obliged to make his decisions for him. Above all, the experimenter should himself be clear about what he wants to know. If he can achieve this and if he has a little statistical knowledge and if the statistician has a little biological knowledge, the foundation of a lasting and helpful partnership will have been laid. It is hoped that this book will help the biological experimenter to talk a little of the statistician's language and so help to bring about a worthwhile collaboration in which each understands and respects the contribution of the other. Alternatively, if the biologist has no statistician to consult, this text may help him carry out for himself some of the operations needed.

1.4   THE MEASUREMENT OF VARIATION

The first task, then, is to clarify the object of the experiment so that it can be designed properly, i.e., in such a way as to yield data useful for the purpose in hand. The data having been obtained, a second task confronts the experimenter—that of estimating the experimental error. The word "error" implies no negligence or fault. There must be variation disturbing the experiment because no plant or animal is identical with any other plant or animal and no plot of ground or pen identical with any other plot of ground or pen. Pieces of apparatus, measuring instruments, observers, and moments of time are likewise all diverse. Consequently, no matter how carefully an experiment is conducted, there must be variation that remains uncontrolled, either because the experimenter has not been able to identify its source or because its elimination would have needed such resources as to make the whole experiment impossible. Phytotrons can enormously reduce environmental variation, just as the use of vegetatively raised plants can reduce genetical variation, but with both plants and animals there will always remain an uncontrolled residue of experimental error. If the aim is to estimate a quantity, on account of the error the result will not be perfectly reliable and analysis will be needed to find out how good the estimate is. If, on the other hand, a hypothesis is under test, it would be most remarkable if the data led to the expected result exactly. Hence, some criterion is needed to judge whether the discrepancy between observation and expectation is within the limits set by the experimental error or whether it is too large to be explained by this action. Either way the error needs to be measured.

This brings up the question of how to describe numerically the differences within a set of figures. There are several ways, but the commonest is illustrated in the following example:

Let the numbers be 9, 6, 5, 8. They add up to 28; there are four of them, so the mean is 7, and their deviations from the mean are respectively $9 - 7 = +2$, $6 - 7 = -1$, $5 - 7 = -2$, and $8 - 7 = +1$. It might appear that a useful measure of variability could be obtained by adding the deviations and taking a mean, but this will not help because they necessarily sum to zero. Another idea might be to ignore the signs and take a mean of the absolute values of the deviations. Certainly this seems quite reasonable, because when the mean is 7 a value of 6 indicates as much error as one of 8, but the arbitrary nature of the calculation produces a quantity with few useful algebraic properties.

Also, although this may not be immediately apparent, a deviation of $+2$ or -2 needs to be given more weight than two deviations of $+1$ or -1, because it implies the action of some large uncontrolled source of variation, whereas a series of small deviations rather confirms the absence of any such source. For these and other reasons, it is usual to eliminate the signs and to give importance to the extreme values by squaring the deviations. In this example the squares are 4, 1, 4, 1, respectively. They sum to 10, thus giving a mean of 2.50. This quantity, however, is not in the original units of measurement, so its square root is taken, i.e., 1.58, which is a useful and easily obtained measure of the dispersion of the original set of figures.

This calculation may be compared with that for another set of figures, namely, 10, 7, 4, 7. The total is 28 as before, and the mean again 7, so the deviations are 3, 0, −3, 0. If the signs are ignored, the deviations still sum to 6 with a mean of 1.50, though most people would agree that the fresh set of figures gives evidence of greater variation than the former. If, however, deviations are squared, the sum comes to 18 instead of 10, which accords with this sense of greater variability in the second case.

It happens that the sum of squared deviations, namely 10 in the first example, can be calculated in another way and one that illuminates the nature of the variation measured. Suppose that the deviations had been taken from some quantity other than the mean, say from 8. They now become $+1, −2, −3, 0$, the sum of their squares now being 14. If, on the other hand, there had been no variation, all the values being equal to 7, then the deviations would have been $−1, −1, −1, −1$, with a sum of squares equal to 4. It will be seen that the difference of these two values, 14 and 4, is 10, the figure obtained previously. This is a general method, as algebra can be used to show.

This approach can be extended. Take all deviations from the actual origin of measurement, i.e., from zero. The sum of squared deviations of the data is $9^2 + 6^2 + 5^2 + 8^2$, or 206. If, however, there had been no variation, the sum of squared deviations would have been $7^2 + 7^2 + 7^2 + 7^2$, or 196, the difference again being 10. The value 196 has here been obtained as 4×7^2; it is, however, better to calculate it as $28^2 \div 4$, where 28 is the total, because this avoids rounding-off errors in working out the mean. In fact, in general, the sum of squared deviations from the mean equals

$$\text{Sum of (data)}^2 - \frac{(\text{total of data})^2}{\text{number of data}}$$

In this form the calculation is easily performed on desk calculators, some models being designed to sum squares readily.

1.5   POPULATION AND SAMPLE

A scientific paper sets out the carcass weights of cattle fed in various ways. The interest a reader finds in it cannot arise from the performance of those particular animals because they are dead, and he knows that whatever cattle he may have to deal with himself, he will never encounter the ones he has been reading about. Nevertheless, he finds the paper interesting because he regards the experimental material as representative of a class about which he wishes to know.

This is true of all experiments. No one examines the behavior of all colonies of bacteria or all plum trees, but only a representative group. An experimenter takes a sample and argues from it to the population from which it came. When mean values are in question this causes no difficulty because the mean of a sample provides an estimate of the population mean. Admittedly the sample is unlikely to contain the largest value that could have been found in the population, but it is also unlikely to contain the smallest. As far as general levels are concerned, the one cancels out the other. The sample will not give exactly the same mean as the population from which it was drawn—this has already been recognized in the discussion of the consequences of error—but it is as likely to be wrong in one direction as the other.

The position is different where measures of variation are concerned. The possibility of a sample missing the large values means that it may underestimate variation and this is reinforced, not nullified, by the possibility of its missing the extreme small ones too. Consequently, the measure of variation that has been given, when calculated from the sample, will underestimate the value in the population about which information is being sought.

This difficulty arises whenever the size of a sample is measured by the number of observations it contains. A better way is to use the number of degrees of freedom. Supposing there are two data; then one piece of information, namely, the difference between them, is sufficient to describe completely the variation of the system. If there are three, two pieces of information will suffice. It does not matter which they are, provided the second is independent of the first. Thus, if $(A - B)$ is known, the description of the total variation is completed by a knowledge of $(A - C)$ or $(B - C)$ or $\frac{1}{2}(A + B) - C$, anything in fact that is additional to what is already known, because it is then possible to work out all differences. On the other hand, it would not help to be told the value of $(B - A)$ because it must equal $-(A - B)$, which is already known. This argument can be continued, and it appears that the variation between n values, whatever value n may take, can be expressed in terms of $(n - 1)$ independent pieces of information. It is said to have $(n - 1)$ "degrees of freedom."

If now, in the worked example, the sum of squared deviations (10) had been divided not by 4 (the number of observations) but by 3 (the number of degrees of freedom, i.e., the potentiality of variation in the system), the result would have been $3\frac{1}{3}$ and the final figure $\sqrt{3\frac{1}{3}} = 1.83$. This would not have measured the variation in the sample, but it would have provided an unbiased estimate of the variation in the population from which the sample came, and it is this that is needed. The value so obtained is called the "standard deviation."

1.6   THE ADDITION OF VARIATION

One advantage of sums of squared deviations and degrees of freedom is that they both can readily be divided, or "partitioned," into parts.

Thus, to take an example, some data were obtained about the mechanical strength of graft unions of pear trees bud-grafted on quince. Grafting is a common practice in horticulture, but with some varieties of pears the union so formed with quince is unsatisfactory and breaks when the trees are about ten years old. The investigation was intended to shed light on the condition of such unions before the weakness becomes apparent in the field. In this experiment some surplus two-year-old trees were taken and placed across two steel supports about 2 feet apart with the graft union in the middle. A band was placed across the union, and weights were suspended from it, these being increased until the tree snapped. A record was then made of the weight used.

The first variety tried was Durondeau, grafted on Quince C. There were four trees, and these broke under weights of 111, 251, 208, and 183 pounds, totaling 753 pounds. There were thus 3 degrees of freedom, and the sum of squared deviations was

$$111^2 + 251^2 + 208^2 + 183^2 - \frac{753^2}{4} = 152\ 075.00 - 141\ 752.25$$
$$= 10\ 322.75$$

It will be noticed that the sum of squared deviations has been worked out to two decimal places more than were obtained from squaring the data. With data as variable as these such precision is not essential, but often the additional decimal places will be useful. Also, the numbers have been written in groups of three digits starting in each direction from the decimal point. When transferring numbers to or from a calculating machine or when copying, it is unwise to try to remember more than three at a time. Where, however, there are only four numbers in all to be transferred, it may be better not to divide them.

For the next graft union, Williams' Bon Chrétien on Quince C, seven trees were available. By similar computation these gave a sum of squared deviations of

$$172^2 + 220^2 + 70^2 + 150^2 + 224^2 + 109^2 + 120^2 - \frac{1\,065^2}{7}$$
$$= 181\,841.00 - 162\,032.14 = 19\,808.86$$

with 6 degrees of freedom.

The last variety was Fertility, also grafted on Quince C, which gave

$$152^2 + 246^2 + 114^2 + 178^2 + 284^2 + 288^2 - \frac{1\,262^2}{6}$$
$$= 291\,900.00 - 265\,440.67 = 26\,459.33$$

with 5 degrees of freedom.

These figures represent variation within the varieties. Between varieties the position is more complicated. First, Durondeau has given four trees with a mean of 188.3. Eliminating variation within the variety, this having already been considered, this variety contributes $4(188.3)^2$, which may equally be written $753^2/4$. Similarly, the other two varieties contribute $1,065^2/7$ and $1,262^2/6$, the sum of these three quantities representing the variation of the variety means from zero. Considering now the variation of the general mean, there are 17 trees with a total of 3,080, so the term is $3,080^2/17$ and the variation of the variety means from the general mean is

$$\frac{753^2}{4} + \frac{1\,065^2}{7} + \frac{1\,262^2}{6} - \frac{3\,080^2}{17}$$
$$= 141\,752.25 + 162\,032.14 + 265\,440.67 - 558\,023.53 = 11\,201.53$$

which has 2 degrees of freedom because there are three varieties.

Now the total variation in the system is the variation of the 17 data from the general mean. Its sum of squared deviations is

$$(\text{Sum of all data squared}) - \frac{3\,080^2}{17}$$
$$= (152\,075.00 + 181\,841.00 + 291\,900.00) - 558\,023.53 = 67\,792.47$$

with 16 degrees of freedom.

It now appears that the components add up correctly, as Table 1.1 shows.

Reflection will show that this is no coincidence. The degrees of freedom of the four components represent pieces of information that are obviously independent of each other and between them represent all the variation

Table 1.1
Partition of variation between varieties and within each variety

Source of variation	df	Sum of squares
Within Durondeau	3	10 322.75
Within Williams' B.C.	6	19 808.86
Within Fertility	5	26 459.33
Between varieties	2	11 201.53
Total	16	67 792.47

possible in the system. Also, the correct addition of the sums of squared deviations is a matter of algebra. This facility of partitioning variation as to both degrees of freedom and sums of squared deviations is one that is capable of wide extension. On it is based the valuable technique of the analysis of variance, which is used in many different forms and for a greater range of problems every year; it is a research tool valued for both its versatility and the subtlety of its application. There is no exaggeration in the assertion that it has made modern experimentation possible.

CHAPTER TWO

ESTIMATES AND TESTS WITH THE ANALYSIS OF VARIANCE

WHAT AN ANALYSIS OF VARIANCE IS FOR AND HOW ITS INTERPRETATION CAN BE ADAPTED TO ANSWER QUESTIONS OF VARIOUS KINDS.

2.1   DESCRIPTION OF THE ANALYSIS OF VARIANCE

One of the most generally useful methods of examining data is the analysis of variance. In essence the approach is to take the total variation to be found among the data and to partition it into a number of components. Necessarily all of these will include contributions from the sources of variation that make up error, but most of them are associated also with some specific source of variation that has been considered in the experimental design. There is always one component, however, which represents only the variation brought about by error; this can be used as a measure for all the rest. It is then possible, when testing, to gauge how far any of the other components have been inflated. Equally, when estimating, the component representing only error can be used as the basis of calculations to decide how good the estimates are.

It should be emphasized that analyses of variance should never be worked out thoughtlessly by routine methods. It is true that there are computing procedures appropriate to a wide range of experiments; these can be learned mechanically and taught to assistants who apply them with even less thought, but such a procedure is full of risks. Each body of data needs to be considered individually, first of all to consider what is error and what is not, then to decide what is being estimated or what is being tested, and finally to detect any special difficulties inherent in the data themselves, e.g., some may be missing or it may be better to turn weights into increments in weight, and so on.

In calculating analyses of variance, certain quantities turn up again and again and are fundamental to the whole approach. The first of these is the sum of squared deviations, which has already been described. It is a direct measure of the amount of variation. The second is the number of degrees of freedom, which represents the number of independent comparisons, i.e.,

14

how much there is in the system that is susceptible to variation. The third is the mean squared deviation, which is the sum of squares divided by the number of degrees of freedom. It therefore provides a basis on which to compare variation in groups of different sizes.

2.2   A CALCULATED EXAMPLE

The data of the pear-grafting experiment and the calculations already carried out can easily be adapted to provide an analysis of variance, though an extremely simple one. In this investigation no regard was paid to any variation apart from that between rootstocks; i.e., error consists of any variation within rootstocks and may be found by putting together the components for variation within each of the three rootstocks separately. This gives the analysis of variance set out in Table 2.1.

Table 2.1
Analysis of variance for the experiment on the strength of graft unions

Source	df	Sum of squares	Mean square
Varieties	2	11 201.53	
Error	14	56 590.94	4 042.21
Total	16	67 792.47	

It will be seen that a fresh column has been added, that for mean squared deviations. This is always obtained for the error line, because it is required for obtaining the standard deviation of the experiment, which here equals $\sqrt{4\,042.21}$ or 63.58. Often other mean squared deviations are needed as well.

The standard deviation of the experiment is one of the most important values that can be obtained from the data, representing as it does the accuracy with which the experiment has been conducted. Usually it is expressed as a percentage of the general mean of the data, in which form it is known as the "coefficient of variation," though this is not popular with mathematicians because in percentage form the value has few useful characteristics. Here there are 17 trees in all, with a total of

$$753 + 1,065 + 1,262 = 3,080$$

the mean being therefore 181.2, and the coefficient of variation about 33 per cent. Only experience can suggest whether this figure is good or bad. With field trials on yields of cereals it would suggest an error so large that the experiment would seem to have been conducted in as slovenly a manner as can be imagined; on the other hand, to anyone used to the enormous variation sometimes encountered in graft-compatibility experiments, it would be a relief to find that it was no larger. Some writers have suggested that coefficients of variation above 10 per cent argue a badly conducted experiment, but no constant limit can be given; experience shows that the level to be expected depends upon species, upon the quantity measured, upon the choice of experimental material, and upon the number of organisms that have gone to make up an experimental unit. This is only to be expected. Twins will give a smaller coefficient of variation than sibs, areas of a hundred palms a lower coefficient than single trees, and so on. An experimenter should rid himself of any preconceived notions and should build up a body of knowledge for his own type of work, both by calculations from his own experiments and by consultation with other workers. In this way he will come to know that his plants or animals are often variable in respect to this measurement but not to that, or that they are more variable, say, in the spring than in the summer, and thus he can derive soundly based criteria for discerning the experiment in which something went wrong.

Nevertheless, although a coefficient of variation of 33 per cent need provoke no comment in experimental work of this kind, it does represent about the upper limit of variability with which it is advisable to work. Where higher values are encountered, it is usually because the quantity under study has been measured on a poor scale; probably lower coefficients of variation would be obtained if, say, the square root of the measurements were analyzed instead. This is a large subject and discussion of it will be postponed until Chapter 4.

However, an analysis of variance is not calculated solely to estimate the coefficient of variation, but also to help in the processes of estimating and testing, whichever may be required. From this point on there can be no standard procedure because everything depends on the purpose for which the data have been collected.

2.3   ESTIMATION PROCEDURES

The experimenter may be well aware that different varieties of pear, when grafted on quince, give unions of greatly varying strengths; consequently he is not asking for anything to be tested. He has merely tried out three varieties and he wishes to know how strong the unions are for each. The first information required is therefore the mean breaking strength of each, which is, Durondeau, 188.3 pounds; Williams' Bon Chrétien, 152.1 pounds; Fertility, 210.7 pounds. Next he wishes to know how well these figures are determined; they are values obtained from samples and could well deviate considerably from the means of the populations. To find out this, he should divide the value of the error mean squared deviation successively by the number of observations in each variety and take the square roots, thus:

Durondeau $\qquad \sqrt{\dfrac{4\,042.21}{4}} = 31.8$

Williams' B. C. $\quad \sqrt{\dfrac{4\,042.21}{7}} = 24.0$

Fertility $\qquad \sqrt{\dfrac{4\,042.21}{6}} = 26.0$

These figures are known as the "standard errors" of the variety means, and they provide a measure of the reliability of the conclusions. A mean differs from its true, or population, value by less than its standard error on about two occasions out of three, so if limits are set up thus:

Durondeau   188.3 ± 31.8, i.e., 156.5 to 220.1
Williams' B. C.   152.1 ± 24.0, i.e., 128.1 to 176.1
Fertility   210.7 ± 26.0, i.e., 184.7 to 236.7

then for each variety there is about one chance in three that the true value lies outside the limits given. If the limits had been set at twice the standard error from the mean, the chances would be about one in twenty; if at three times the standard error, about one in three hundred. It appears then that these means have not been estimated with any high precision.

Limits like those just indicated are known as "confidence limits," and the values within them are said to lie in the "confidence belt" for whatever probability level has been adopted. Whatever limits are used, there must always be a small chance that the experimenter's confidence has been misplaced and the true value lies outside the belt, but, if all has been done correctly, the probability of this happening is a measurable one.

The above rule for calculating the confidence limits is, however, only approximate, because no account has been taken of the fact that the mean squared deviation for error is itself an estimated quantity liable to wrong evaluation just as the mean can be wrongly evaluated and for the same reasons. However, the greater the number of degrees of freedom upon which the error is based, the better the evaluation will be. Confidence limits can be worked out better if this is allowed for, and this can be done by using the values of t set out in Appendix I. (A fuller table will be found in Fisher and Yates, Table III.) Thus in this example there are 14 degrees of freedom for error. If limits are required such that there is only one chance in twenty ($P = 0.05$) of the true value lying outside them, it appears that t equals 2.145. Multiplying this by the standard error gives the distance of the confidence limits from the mean, i.e., the confidence belts are these:

Durondeau	$188.3 \pm 2.145(31.8)$,	i.e., 120.1 to 256.5
Williams' B. C.	$152.1 \pm 2.145(24.0)$,	i.e., 100.6 to 203.6
Fertility	$210.7 \pm 2.145(26.0)$,	i.e., 154.9 to 266.5

An experimenter might, however, know that Fertility grafted on quince gave a better union than the others and would perhaps want to find out how much weaker the other two were, i.e., he would be interested not in the means themselves but in the extent to which they differed from a standard. A similar situation arises when the general level of values varies a lot from one experiment to another for reasons that do not affect the experiment. Thus, if a study is made of the effects of different substances in inhibiting the germination of spores of a species of fungus, it may not be thought worthwhile to standardize carefully the temperature at which the experiments take place so long as it held constant within each separate experiment. Accordingly the actual percentage germination for each substance will mean little, only differences within experiments being important.

To take the case of the pear-grafting experiment, the other two varieties fall short of Fertility in strength of union by amounts equal to:

Durondeau   22.4 lb
Williams' B. C.   58.6 lb
These have standard errors of

$$\sqrt{(\tfrac{1}{4} + \tfrac{1}{6})(4\,042.21)} = 41.0$$
$$\text{and} \quad \sqrt{(\tfrac{1}{7} + \tfrac{1}{6})(4\,042.21)} = 35.4$$

respectively. Confidence limits for the differences of means are calculated from their standard errors using the same procedures as for means themselves.

2.4   THE F TEST AND THE IDEA OF SIGNIFICANCE

Turning now to testing, the experimenter may want a comprehensive test that tells him whether the treatments regarded as a whole have had any effect on the measurements that make up the data. In such circumstances, he will use the F test. In the analysis of variance the variety mean squared deviation was $\frac{1}{2}(11\ 201.53) = 5\ 600.77$, a figure somewhat larger than the corresponding one for error. Although the "source" for this line is given as "varieties" it should be borne in mind that error in the sense of uncontrolled variation permeates everything, so the source is really (error + varieties). In this instance the variety mean square is indeed rather larger than that for error, the ratio being 1.39, a quantity denoted by the symbol F. Such an excess, however, means very little, and an experimenter who wants to know if it is true that different varieties give graft unions of varying strengths should not regard it as evidence of such an effect. The value of F should be looked up in tables (Appendix II or those of Fisher and Yates, Table V); from these it appears that with a numerator having 2 degrees of freedom and a denominator having 14, the value of F could be as high as 1.81 on one occasion in five ($P = 0.2$) purely by chance, even though there were no varietal effects to inflate the numerator. For P equal to 0.05, i.e., on one occasion in twenty, F could reach 3.74 by chance. If it does, it is usual to say that the result is "significant" and to mark the value of F with a single asterisk. This means that a skeptic who wishes to deny the genuineness of the differences, asserting that the data just happened to fall out like that, is believing in a one-in-twenty coincidence. Of course, he may be right. The writer once found a difference at $P = 0.001$, only to learn later that an assistant had forgotten to apply the treatments. Nevertheless, the claim to significance does present a choice: *either* the treatments have had the effect attributed to them *or* a coincidence has arisen with stated odds against it.

Continuing with the tables, it appears that for 2 and 14 degrees of freedom the value of F will exceed 6.51 by chance on only one occasion in one hundred ($P = 0.01$); such a value is said to be "highly significant" and is indicated by two asterisks. By chance, F will exceed 11.78 on only one occasion in one thousand ($P = 0.001$); this is said to be "very highly significant" and is shown by three asterisks.

The idea of significance is so fundamental in any testing of hypotheses that it needs to be examined closely. A significance level is *the probability of the result having arisen entirely by chance*, the treatments having had nothing to do with it. Essentially the argument is an application of "Occam's razor," i.e., the doctrine that entities of thought should not be multiplied unnecessarily. As long as it is reasonable to explain phenomena in terms of experimental error, no effects of treatments need be postulated.

It is now necessary to gauge the value of P at which skepticism breaks down and it is conceded that the treatments must have had an effect. Insofar as doubt is something personal to the individual, no rules can be given. Certainly there can be no question of a hard and fast distinction between significance and nonsignificance, as if P being equal to 0.049 proved conclusively that the treatments had an effect, whereas P equal to 0.051 exploded all reasonable belief in their efficacy. The recent tendency to get away from a single significance level and to use one, two, or three asterisks for P reaching 0.05, 0.01, and 0.001 respectively is therefore a good one because it emphasizes that there is a gradation in the strength of evidence. It is not certain, however, that it goes far enough, because the steps are still rather large ones. Also, suspicion that an effect exists can be quite reasonable even though P is quite a lot larger than 0.05. Accordingly it is here recommended that where the existence of an effect has been tested and P has proved to be less than about 0.2, that fact should be stated in any report. Such a level of significance will not convince anyone with a robustly skeptical attitude, but to someone who is already half-convinced by other evidence it may be the last detail needed for belief.

It must be admitted that this broad-minded attitude on the part of an experimenter breaks down when he reports a second investigation continuing the first, because he must then make his own position clear. If he is quite content with a low level of significance (say $P > 0.05$), he should set out fully the reasons for his readiness to believe; if, on the other hand, he is still skeptical, e.g., he does not believe though P has proved to be small, again some explanation is called for.

It is sometimes said that the significance of a difference does not matter much compared with its practical importance, but this is something of a half-truth. The classical role of an experiment is to justify a line of thought, and for this the concept of significance is required. Thus, the observation that the incidence of smallpox was less among dairy maids than among other people led to a useful line of thought, not because the difference was large in absolute magnitude, though it may have been, but because it could not be dismissed as a coincidence.

Nevertheless, for an experiment intended to lead directly to an improvement in current practice, differences that are of importance should be commensurate with those the experiment can demonstrate. Here an overelaborate experiment can establish differences that are significant though they are of little practical importance, or a scrappy one can dismiss differences as nonsignificant though they would be most important if their genuineness could be confirmed. Accordingly, in reporting experiments of a practical nature, care should be taken to consider the results from both points of view. However, no conflict should arise if the experiment has been designed to be of the right size in the first place.

2.5 THE t TEST IN ITS TWO FORMS

The F test applies when all the differences between treatment means are equally important, but often certain differences have a special status arising from the nature of the investigation. For example, a herbicide may be applied at several concentrations, say none at all and at the recommended rate, with a third treatment of half the recommended rate included for some special purpose, e.g., to see if a reasonable measure of weed control could not be obtained with markedly reduced residual effects on future crops or to check that cheaper applications would suffice at certain seasons when weeds are especially susceptible. In such a case, the comparison of the effects of full application and zero application remains important, providing as it does a means of judging if the herbicide does in fact have an effect at the recommended dose and, if so, how large the effect is. If the two treatments had been used by themselves, an F test would have been useful, but the addition of a third treatment has given 2 degrees of freedom instead of 1, and the F criterion provides a means of testing them only together. What is needed is a method for testing in isolation the degree of freedom for the difference of the two extreme treatments. Similar difficulties arise in many other contexts. Whenever there are more than two treatments, there is always the possibility of wanting to look at only a few of the treatment degrees of freedom or of wanting to look at certain ones in isolation. The general question of partitioning the treatment degrees of freedom is a large one, and it will be discussed in more generality later, but the t test provides one approach to the problem and will be considered here.

The t test is of use when certain comparisons have a special importance arising from the logic of the problem. Thus, in the pear-grafting trial it might well have been that Williams' Bon Chrétien and Fertility were introduced because it was known that graft unions for these two varieties behave in very different ways in mature trees, and the question had arisen whether the same difference could be observed in young ones, Durondeau being introduced as an intermediate variety. In such circumstances it would be reasonable to test the difference between Williams' Bon Chrétien and

Fertility separately. The difference between the means is divided by its own standard error, the ratio being termed t, thus

$$t = \frac{58.6}{35.4} = 1.66$$

This figure is compared with values set out in tables (e.g., Appendix I, or Table III in Fisher and Yates) for 14 degrees of freedom in the error. It appears that the figure could reach 1.345 by chance on one occasion in five ($P = 0.2$) and 1.761 on one occasion in ten ($P = 0.1$), so the level of significance is not high.

It should be emphasized that this test is valid only because the comparison investigated was "nominated," i.e., because it was indicated by the logic of the experimental situation and was singled out before any data were obtained. It is true that the difference nominated also happened to be the largest within the set of means, but this is irrelevant. Plainly, if all possible differences within the set are tested separately and each is given one chance in twenty of appearing significant, something will pass the test eventually if only enough differences can be devised; this would be so even if the data were in fact taken from a table of random numbers. The position is not changed by all the differences being found and only the largest being tested, because that is one that would have passed if all had been tested. There is no escape from this; a difference should only be examined if it corresponds to some effect about which information is being sought.

Several writers have suggested "protective levels of significance" or the use of levels of significance "experiment-wise." The idea is to test everything at a small value of P, so that the chance of something or other proving significant in the experiment *as a whole* is 0.05 or 0.01 or whatever is desired. Admittedly there are circumstances where this is a useful approach, but basically it is a mathematical attempt to solve a problem that is not mathematical in nature. A good investigator does not throw a heap of treatments into an experiment with no thought of any relationship between them, ready to regard one difference as being as important or as interesting as any other. On the contrary he gives great thought to what should be included. The difference between treatments A and B will tell him one thing, that between B and C something else, while that between A and C is due to more than one cause and is of no interest, but is known only because both A and C happen to be in the same experiment. If he is really ready to go fishing with a statistical technique in order to find something—it does not matter what— to declare significant, he should not be engaged in research.

Experimenters are sometimes troubled by discrepancies between conclusions based on the F test and those based on the t test. If there are only two treatments, i.e., only 1 degree of freedom for treatments, one test will always lead to exactly the same result as the other, but if there are 3 or more, the t test often appears to be more sensitive. What has happened, usually, is that a t test has been carried out on a difference that is especially under study and is larger than any of the others, and this has proved to be a more sensitive procedure than using the F test, in which all differences are on an equal footing and the large ones are diluted by the small ones. As long as the t test is being correctly used, this greater sensitivity is justified.

A vexing question is that of the "least significant difference." If the standard error of a difference is multiplied by the value of t corresponding to a certain P, and if the difference itself is found to exceed the product, then by the t test it is significant at the level indicated by P. Thus, in the pear-grafting experiment, the standard error of the difference of the means for Williams' Bon Chrétien and Fertility was 35.4. For 14 degrees of freedom and P equal to 0.05, t equals 2.145. If, then, the difference had proved to exceed $75.9 (= 2.145 \times 35.4)$, the two varieties would have been held to differ significantly. Plainly, this is no more than the t test carried out in another way. However, it is a very convenient way when there are a number of comparisons, all with the same standard error, a state of affairs that often arises when all the treatment means are based on the same number of obser-vations. The objection to the least significant difference is that it is some-times applied by unskilled interpreters of data to all differences, whether nominated or not. However, the possible misuse of a technique is no reason for avoiding it altogether.

It will be noticed that the least significant difference equals the distance between a difference of means and one of its confidence limits. This is no coincidence. If the confidence belt of a difference includes zero, then that is—at the stated significance level—a possible value, i.e., there may be no difference.

Sometimes, as here, the argument can be taken further. The t test, as described above, would give the same result whichever variety had had the stronger union, but if Fertility had proved to be the weaker, the result would in fact have been attributed to chance. When differences will be accepted only if they are in a specified direction, the significance level, i.e., the probability of finding something by chance, is halved; so, in this instance, the significance level, which appeared to approach one in ten, really approaches one in twenty.

What happens in a one-sided test is that the experimenter really wishes to use a significance level, P, but he actually enters the t tables at $2P$, having made a pact with himself to ignore all results that go the "wrong way." This is a rather extreme position. He is in fact declaring that, however strong the evidence, there are some things which he will steadfastly refuse to believe. It would be more reasonable for him to say that he is readier to believe if the difference goes one way than if it goes the other, and that he is therefore using different significance levels according to the sign of the effect when found. If these levels are P_+ and P_-, the overall probability of finding an effect spuriously is $\frac{1}{2}(P_+ + P_-)$. However, whatever he does, the procedure must be nominated beforehand; he must not choose it after his opinions have been affected by the data before him.

2.6   MULTIPLE-RANGE TESTS

Because the least significant difference may not be used indiscriminately, but only for comparisons nominated by the logic of the experimental situation, it is not suitable for dividing a series of treatments into groups, though this is sometimes required. Supposing, for example, that a measurable character is believed to depend on only a few genes, e.g., the heights of Mendel's peas. Then a test is requiredth at will show up the segregation, putting together in groups phenotypes that are similar in respect to the character under study. In the past this has often been done using a least significant difference and comparing its value with all the observed differences, but for the reason given such indiscriminate use is wrong. Various other ways have been suggested instead, and the generic name for them is "multiple-range tests." The one to be described here is that due to Duncan, who published tables,[1] analogous to those of t, that enable his test to be used.

To take an example, an experiment was conducted on a range of new apple rootstocks. There were six of them, *A* to *F*, all crosses, with the dwarfing rootstock, Malling IX, as one of the parents. There were many other crosses, but these six were markedly vigorous, unlike Malling IX, and were being studied for their possible commercial usefulness in the vigorous class. To ascertain their vigor, each was grafted with a range of four scion varieties, and the trunk girth of each tree was measured and converted to logarithms, which were averaged. This was done three times; as a result the following rootstock means were found:

D	*C*	*E*	*A*	*F*	*B*
1.097	1.180	1.197	1.291	1.372	1.430

[1] D. B. Duncan, *Biometrics*, 11:3–4.

Each of these means has a standard error of 0.0429, based on 10 degrees of freedom for error.

The extreme range is that between B and D and equals (1.430 − 1.097) or 0.333. Duncan's tables show that in a homogeneous group of six ($p = 6$), for a probability level of 0.05 with 10 degrees of freedom for error ($n = 10$), the range should not exceed 3.46 times the standard error of a mean. This equals 3.46 × 0.0429, or 0.148, so B and D do not belong to the same group. Leaving aside D for the moment, the range lies between B and C and equals 0.250. For p equal to 5, the multiplier is 3.43, so the range should not exceed 0.147, and C also must be regarded as different from B. For p equal to 4, the range can go up to 3.37 × 0.0429, or 0.145; for a set of three it can go to 3.30 × 0.0429, or 0.142. Hence, while E must be accounted different from B, A and B could well be in the same group and this could obviously include F as well.

The whole process is now repeated disregarding B. D, C, and E must lie in different groups from F, but A could be in the same. A is now taken as having the largest mean; D is different, but C and E could be the same. Passing to E, it appears that D could lie in the same group and this could therefore include C as well. The most rational interpretation of all this is to take A, F, and B as one group and D, C, and E as another, while noting that C, E, and A do not differ significantly.

It is necessary here to say bluntly that in this particular context the above analysis is a lot of pretentious nonsense. Those who work with rootstocks know that they do not form vigor groups, but present a continuous spectrum of vigor. If there had been 1,000 rootstocks instead of 6, all the gaps would have been filled in. In fact the analysis has been directed to determining groups when there is no reason to expect any.

This criticism is directed not at the test itself but at the present vogue for using multiple-range tests as a matter of course, whether they are appropriate or not. In many genetical contexts the object is indeed to form clusters corresponding to the phenotypes. Where there is reason to expect groups, the multiple-range tests provide an excellent means of finding them and their use is strongly to be recommended. It is, on the other hand, an unjustifiable evasion of thought to use them regardless of context.

2.7   SEQUENTIAL EXPERIMENTS

It sometimes happens that an experiment is best carried out by stages, with an analysis of data after each stage. Thus, the value of the experimental material may require that the investigation come to an end as soon as a conclusion has been reached. Indeed, in a medical context this can be a most compelling consideration; ethical reasons absolutely prevent a practitioner from prescribing a treatment when an alternative one is known to be better. At the start of an experiment, when no one can say which treatment is to be preferred, it may suffice to take patients in pairs and to allocate one or another of the alternatives at random, but after a time this would be wrong because experience could guide the choice. Another example of such experimentation arises when a scheme of investigation has been completed, but with inconclusive results, and there is a tantalizing hope that a few more data would clinch the matter. Sometimes, too, an effect of treatments seems so apparent at an early stage that there is a strong temptation to call the rest of the investigation off as a waste of effort.

The great danger is of going on till a desired result is obtained and then stopping. With nonsequential methods this cannot arise; the experimenter declares that he will study so many plants or animals under each treatment, and he abides by the outcome. If sequential methods are to be used without bias, an objective rule is required. This rule must provide not only for stopping when a positive result has appeared, but also for stopping when it has become clear that no such result can reasonably be expected; otherwise the experimenter will go on taking more and more data in unavailing efforts to demonstrate nonexistent effects. This calls for more preliminary decisions than are needful with nonsequential methods. There it suffices to specify a "significance level," i.e., the probability that can be tolerated of appearing to show a result when there really should not be one. With sequential methods it is also necessary to specify a tolerable level of probability of missing a real difference, should one exist.

It is not possible in a book of this size to discuss sequential methods at length, but only to warn the reader about using ordinary tests in a sequential situation and to give one simple example to illustrate what has been said.

The test to be illustrated is the analog of the two-sided t test, tables for which have been published.[2] Data will be taken from an experiment[3] in which each woman suffering from pregnancy toxaemia admitted to a hospital was paired with a normal woman, and inquiries were made as to the amount of fiber in their diets. For reasons that will appear in Chapter 4, the fiber was analyzed not as gram weight but as the square root of this. The calculations are set out in Table 2.2.

    [2] U.S. National Bureau of Standards, Tables to Facilitate Sequential t Tests, Applied Mathematics Series 7, 1951.
    [3] J. F. Howeler and A. D. Hewson, Dietary Fibre and Toxaemia of Pregnancy, *Medical Journal of Australia*, June 1, 1957.

First some decisions need to be made about probability levels. It was decided to work to a significance level, α, of 0.05, i.e., to accept that probability of finding a spurious difference. It was decided also to accept a probability, β, of 0.05 of missing a difference if there were really one as large as four-fifths of the standard deviation ($\delta = 0.8$). This latter choice can be made only where it is possible to make a reasonable guess about how large a standard deviation might arise.

It is now necessary to work out two quantities,

$$L_A = \log_e \frac{1 - \beta}{\alpha}$$

$$L_B = \log_e \frac{\beta}{1 - \alpha}$$

These equal $- \log_e 19$ and $\log_e 19$ respectively. The figures for $\delta = 0.8$ are on pages 51 to 58 of the tables. The column for $- \log 19$ starts from the case when 10 paired comparisons have been made, that for $\log 19$ when six pairs of data are available. Accordingly, six pairs of women must be studied before any question of stopping can arise.

The first column of Table 2.2 gives the series number for each pair of observations. The next two columns give the data, that for a healthy pregnancy coming first in each pair; the fourth column gives the difference, and the fifth the square of the difference. The next two columns give accumulated figures for the fourth and fifth columns.

It is the last three columns that show the working of the test. The middle one shows the criterion; this is the figure in column 6 squared and divided by the number in column 7. It is flanked by limits taken from the tables; if it goes over either, the experiment is brought to an end.

There is no need to calculate the criterion before $n = 6$, because there are no limits to cross. When this point is reached, the evidence in favor of there being more fiber in the diet of the women without toxaemia is very slight, and it might be expected that as soon as a lower limit appeared, the criterion would be below it; but its value rises as evidence comes in supporting a difference, and by $n = 10$ it appears that either limit might be the one to be crossed. During the next five observations two pieces of evidence are encountered that contradict the general trend, and the criterion remains steady, but it begins to rise again, till at $n = 20$ a large difference supporting the trend causes it to jump. Finally, with two strong pieces of supporting evidence, the conclusion is reached that there is indeed a difference in fiber contents of diets at $n = 26$. Plainly, it is the women with pregnancy toxaemia who have had the lower amount of fiber.

Table 2.2
Computations for a sequential *t* test

(1)	(2)	(3)	(4)	(5)	(6)	(7)	(8)	(9)	(10)
No.	Data		Diff.	Diff.²	Ac-cumu-lated Diff.	Accumu-lated Diff.²	Limit	Cri-terion	Limit
1	2.61	1.70	+0.91	0.8281	0.91	0.8281			
2	2.95	2.42	+0.53	0.2809	1.44	1.1090			
3	2.60	2.84	−0.24	0.0576	1.20	1.1666			
4	2.05	2.63	−0.58	0.3364	0.62	1.5030			
5	3.08	3.41	−0.33	0.1089	0.29	1.6119			
6	2.06	1.63	+0.43	0.1849	0.72	1.7968		0.289	5.831
7	3.82	1.96	+1.86	3.4596	2.58	5.2564		1.266	5.718
8	2.55	2.46	+0.09	0.0081	2.67	5.2645		1.354	5.660
9	2.96	1.91	+1.05	1.1025	3.72	6.3670		2.173	5.641
10	4.26	2.26	+2.00	4.0000	5.72	10.3670	0.086	3.156	5.650
11	2.68	2.39	+0.29	0.0841	6.01	10.4511	0.193	3.456	5.680
12	3.02	3.55	−0.53	0.2809	5.48	10.7320	0.302	2.798	5.727
13	1.93	1.40	+0.53	0.2809	6.01	11.0129	0.412	3.280	5.787
14	1.87	1.94	−0.07	0.0049	5.94	11.0178	0.525	3.202	5.857
15	2.52	1.62	+0.90	0.8100	6.84	11.8278	0.640	3.956	5.935
16	2.14	1.71	+0.43	0.1849	7.27	12.0127	0.757	4.400	6.021
17	2.20	2.75	−0.55	0.3025	6.72	12.3152	0.877	3.667	6.112
18	1.97	1.71	+0.26	0.0676	6.98	12.3828	0.999	3.935	6.208
19	2.85	2.61	+0.24	0.0576	7.22	12.4404	1.122	4.190	6.308
20	3.65	1.68	+1.97	3.8809	9.19	16.3213	1.246	5.175	6.412
21	2.26	2.36	−0.10	0.0100	9.09	16.3313	1.372	5.059	6.519
22	2.80	1.76	+1.04	1.0816	10.13	17.4129	1.500	5.893	6.628
23	2.03	2.01	+0.02	0.0004	10.15	17.4133	1.628	5.916	6.740
24	1.88	1.92	−0.04	0.0016	10.11	17.4149	1.756	5.869	6.854
25	2.36	1.25	+1.11	1.2321	11.22	18.6470	1.886	6.751	6.970
26	2.88	1.77	+1.11	1.2321	12.33	19.8791	2.016	7.648	7.087

By this time the value of *t* has climbed to 3.25, which would be regarded as highly significant if the experimenter had declared beforehand that she would decide after 26 pairs had been taken.

In this particular instance there was no medical necessity for using a sequential approach, since the investigation did not involve treating patients in any unusual way. (As a matter of fact the approach was nonsequential, a sample of 30 having been decided upon in advance; the figures have here been used to illustrate the way evidence built up as data were obtained.)

However, there are many instances when an investigator would feel easier in his mind if he could avoid unnecessary experimentation.

Of course, in a sequential experiment there must be no tampering with the sequence. Data should be accepted as they come. Otherwise the experimenter can force the criterion over a limit by choosing first those data that support a desired conclusion, thus virtually discarding those that contradict it, and bringing the investigation to an end without considering them.

The real conclusion of this chapter is that no test or estimate is generally valid. Unless it is suggested by the logic of the experimental situation, any test, estimate, or standard error is nothing but illogicality with mathematical adornments. On the other hand, if any of them does fit a problem, it may become a tool of the highest value, giving precise mathematical form to a process that otherwise can be only a groping after conclusions sensed dimly by intuition.

CHAPTER THREE

ANALYSIS OF VARIANCE FOR ORTHOGONAL DESIGNS

THE MAIN CLASSES OF EXPERIMENTAL
DESIGNS. HOW THEY ENABLE ACCURACY TO BE
IMPROVED WHILE STILL PERMITTING THE USE
OF THE ANALYSIS OF VARIANCE.

BLESSED ARE THE SIMPLE, FOR THEY SHALL ENJOY MUCH
PEACE.   THOMAS À KEMPIS   "THE IMITATION OF CHRIST" I, XI

3.1   SOME DEFINITIONS

The simplest experimental designs in ordinary use are the so-called "orthogonal" ones. Before describing them, however, there are some definitions that can usefully be given.

First of all, a *treatment* refers to any difference between the experimental units that has been deliberately introduced so that its effect can be observed. To many biologists this seems a puzzling use of the word. Thus, when an experiment is said to have two treatments, injecting penicillin and not injecting it, a biologist may ask how doing nothing for a patient can be called treating him. Again, in the pear-grafting experiment, a statistician would refer to the three varieties as "treatments," defending his use of the term by pointing out that these are the differences under study. Medical men especially find this usage puzzling, because by "treatment" they mean not just doing something, but doing something that is expected to be beneficial. They are therefore astonished when feeding rats on a vitamin-deficient diet is referred to as a treatment. However, in the parlance of the statistician the word is being used correctly, and it is now too late to ask him to mend his ways.

In fact, to a statistician, sources of variation are associated with either (1) treatments, i.e., differences deliberately introduced so that their effects can be studied, (2) devices such as blocks, which will be described later, intended to remove irrelevant variation, or (3) error, i.e., sources that are uncontrolled.

Another word statisticians use so as to puzzle everyone else is "plot." Modern statistical methods began in agriculture, where treatments are applied to small pieces of land, correctly termed "plots." With the spread of the subject, experimental units came to be very different, but the word remains and is used to describe any unit to which treatments are applied. Thus, to a research worker in veterinary science, a plot may be the individual cow, if he is administering a drug, or a herd, if he is studying the effect of different kinds of pasture, or a small area of hide, if he is interested

32

in comparing different kinds of tuberculin. Similarly, to a plant physiologist a plot can be one cell, one leaf, a sample of leaves, one shoot, one plant, a hundred plants, or a forest; it all depends on the scale of his experiment. He may measure individual cells, individual leaves, or individual trees, but this does not determine his plot. The word refers to the unit to which treatments are applied, not to the unit that is measured.

Another word requiring definition is "variate," which is used for the quantities actually being submitted to analysis. Thus, the data may consist of two measurements made on each plot. Either measurement could be analyzed; the one which is becomes a variate. Quite often, however, the variate is not one of the sets of data, but is, say, a ratio of the two or is obtained by multiplying one by the square of the other.

Looking back for a moment on the analysis of variance for the one-way classification (Table 2.1), it appears that all the sums of squared deviations were obtained from three quantities. First there was T, the sum of data squared. Then there was T_1, formed by squaring the total for each treatment, dividing by the number of data for the treatment, and adding the quotients; and T_0, obtained by squaring the grand total and dividing by the number of data in the experiment as a whole. Then the treatment sum of squared deviations equalled $T_1 - T_0$, the corresponding value for error was $T - T_1$, and for total, $T - T_0$.

These three quantities, T, T_1, and T_0, have much in common and will be called "summation terms." Given a series of totals, a summation term is formed by

1. Squaring each of the totals
2. Dividing each square by the number of data on which the total is based
3. Adding the quotients

In T each value to be squared was itself a single datum, so step (2) had no effect. In T_0 there was only one quotient, so step (3) was not needed.

If all the totals are based on the same number of data, the process can be simplified to this:

1. Squaring each of the totals
2. Adding the squares
3. Dividing the sum by the number of data in each total

Of these summation terms, T is called the "total term" and represents the variation of the data from zero. T_1 is the "treatment term"; its suffix represents the first classification, which in this example happens to be the only one. The term itself measures the variation of the treatment means from zero. T_0 has a suffix representing the absence of classification, all data being merged into one grand total. It is called the "correction term" and represents the variation of the general mean from zero.

In general, the analysis of variance for a one-way classification is that given in Table 3.1.

Table 3.1
Analysis of variance for a one-way classification

Source	df^1	Sum of squares
Treatments	$t - 1$	$T_1 - T_0$
Error	$N - t$	$T - T_1$
Total	$N - 1$	$T - T_0$

[1] Here t is the number of treatments and N the number of data.

3.2 ORTHOGONAL TWO-WAY CLASSIFICATIONS

In the pear-grafting experiment the plots could be classified in only one way. If somebody had pointed to one of them and had asked what was known about it, the only available information would have been the treatment applied to it. No doubt observation would have suggested other classifications, but nothing else was taken into account in the design of the experiment.

Plainly it is not satisfactory to assign to error all sources of variation other than treatments; consequently designs with one-way classification are not usual. In practice, the plots are usually grouped into "blocks," chosen so that there is as little variation as possible within blocks and as much as possible between them. For example, in a nutritional experiment on rats it might be thought advisable to form blocks of animals of about the same age and weight, or in a learning experiment to form blocks of children of the same age and sex with the same intelligence quotient. There is no statistical rule in this matter. Everyone must be guided by his own experience and his own biological knowledge.

The blocks having been formed, other sources of variation should as far as possible be associated with them. Thus, if the end of a working day is approaching, a wise experimenter will finish measuring the plots of one block and will not start on those of the next, so that any development overnight will be associated with blocks, differences due to it being eliminated along with those already associated with the blocks. Again, it may not be possible for all spore cultures in an experiment to be placed in the same incubator, but this does not matter so long as all cultures in a block are kept together—if possible, on the same shelf of one incubator. Perhaps leaf samples have been collected with a view to counting the insects on them; probably some observers will be sharper-eyed and will find more insects than the others, but this need not disturb the experiment if in each block all the samples are counted by the same person. In fact, the blocks are used as a sort of rubbish dump, all unwanted variation as far as possible being associated with them, so that elimination of block differences eliminates other irrelevant variation as well.

The commonest type of two-way classification occurs in the design known as "randomized blocks." It is by far the most useful of all designs and can cope successfully with many of the experimental situations that arise in practice. Blocks are formed, each containing as many plots as there are treatments. Then in each block one plot is assigned at random to each treatment. Such a design may be described as using an "orthogonal" two-way classification of blocks and treatments. The word comes from mathematics, and basically it means "at right angles" but it has a derived meaning in mechanics where much depends upon a property of two orthogonal forces, namely, that the effect of either may be studied without inquiring into the effect of the other. It is the same with the classifications such as these. Each treatment occurs once in each block. Consequently, differences between blocks will not affect differences between treatments. Likewise, each block contains each treatment once, so differences between blocks are unaffected by differences between treatments.

Actually, a two-way classification is orthogonal if each block is made up in the same way with respect to treatments, e.g., if each contains two plots of treatment A, three of B, and one of C. Such designs possess many of the properties associated with randomized blocks.

When an experiment is designed in an orthogonal two-way classification, the analysis of variance for the data is only slightly more complicated than when there is one classification. Because the two classifications are orthogonal, each may be examined separately. Altogether four summation terms are needed, namely,

T, based on the data

T_1, based on the block totals, blocks being the first classification

T_2, based on the treatment totals, treatments being the second classification

T_0, based on the grand total

When enumerating the classifications, treatments are placed last and are then adjacent to error in the analysis, which takes the form shown in Table 3.2. The error line has been obtained by difference, but in any arithmetical example it should be obtained independently from the formulas given. For randomized blocks, $N = bt$, so the error degrees of freedom are $(b - 1)(t - 1)$, i.e., it is necessary only to multiply the degrees of freedom for blocks and treatments. If everything now adds up correctly, the whole analysis is checked, supposing that there is no doubt about the correctness of the summation terms.

Table 3.2
Analysis of variance for an orthogonal
two-way classification

Source	df[1]	Sum of squares
Blocks	$b - 1$	$T_1 - T_0$
Treatments	$t - 1$	$T_2 - T_0$
Error	$N - b - t + 1$	$T - T_1 - T_2 + T_0$
Total	$N - 1$	$T - T_0$

[1] Here b is the number of blocks, t the number of treatments, and N the number of plots.

To take an example from plant physiology, a research program was projected about the effect of growth substances on peas. As a first step it was decided to find which substances affected the development of peas, and an experiment was designed in randomized blocks. In it, a range of substances was compared with an untreated control. Seeds of the variety Greenfeast were germinated in vermiculite and planted in boxes, plots consisting of four plants. Supplementary light was available and was used to make day length up to eighteen hours, thus specifying the environment. As each plant developed, two applications of one microgram of one of the substances were made on the first expanded leaf, and thereafter a number of observations were made, among them the one to be analyzed here, namely, the number of the node with the first initiated flower. Data were as in Table 3.3, each figure representing the total for the four plants. The use of the total for the plot instead of the mean per plant has two advantages: it (1) avoids rounding-off errors and (2) reduces the number of divisions needed, these being carried out at the end.

Table 3.3
Data from an experiment on the efficacy of various growth substances

	Block				
	I	II	III	IV	
Untreated control	60	62	61	60	243
Gibberellic acid	65	65	68	65	263
Kinetin	63	61	61	60	245
Indole acetic acid	64	67	63	61	255
Adenine sulphate	62	65	62	64	253
Maleic hydrazide	61	62	62	65	250
	375	382	377	375	1509

The first step is to work out the block and treatment totals and to check that they add up to the same grand total. It is now a straightforward matter to find the summation terms, as follows:

T, the total term
$$= 60^2 + 62^2 + \cdots + 62^2 + 65^2$$
$$= 94\ 993.00$$

T_1, the block term
$$= \tfrac{1}{6}(375^2 + 382^2 + 377^2 + 375^2)$$
$$= 94\ 883.83$$

T_2, the treatment term
$$= \tfrac{1}{4}(243^2 + 263^2 + 245^2 + 255^2 + 253^2 + 250^2)$$
$$= 94\ 944.25$$

T_0, the correction term $= \tfrac{1}{24}(1509^2) = 94\ 878.38$

The analysis of variance is therefore that in Table 3.4. From it, all the estimates and tests described in Chapter 2 can be made, apart from the sequential t test for which tables are not available, though it may be noted that the toxaemia experiment described was really in randomized blocks, pairs of women forming the blocks. The block classification, being orthogonal to treatments, does not affect comparisons between treatments. In this experiment the question is the extent to which each of the various substances tested has shown itself to give results different from those of the untreated control. Accordingly, a series of t tests is required, all with the standard error

$$\sqrt{2.887(\tfrac{1}{4} + \tfrac{1}{4})} = 1.201$$

so here a least significant difference would be helpful. For $P = 0.05$ and 15 degrees of freedom for error, t equals 2.131 and the least significant difference equals 2.56. Treatment means, worked out to one decimal place more than in the data, are given in Table 3.5.

Table 3.4
Analysis of variance for the experiment on the efficacy of various growth substances

Source	df	Sum of squares	Mean square
Blocks	3	5.45	
Treatments	5	65.87	
Error	15	43.30	2.887
Total	23	114.62	

Table 3.5
Treatment means for the experiment on the efficacy of various growth substances

Treatment	Mean	Diff. from control
Untreated control	60.8	—
Gibberellic acid	65.8	5.0
Kinetin	61.3	0.5
Indole acetic acid	63.8	3.0
Adenine sulphate	63.3	2.5
Maleic hydrazide	62.5	1.7

Clearly, gibberellic acid has had an effect; indeed, the difference is significant at the much higher level of $P = 0.001$. Indole acetic acid also shows a significant difference ($P = 0.05$) from the control and adenine sulphate comes very near it. This analysis does not suggest that much attention need be paid to kinetin and maleic hydrazide. It is true that both gave a slight increase in the mean node number, the difference going the same way as for the other substances, but the effects were so small that they could well be due to chance. Of course, these substances may affect other characteristics of the plants.

In presenting these results it would be better to divide everything, means and least significant difference, by four, so that they are expressed in terms of a quantity that will be clearly understood. At present they refer to the total of four plants; it would be better if they referred to means per plant. It will be noticed that the trial was sensitive enough to show up clearly differences between treatments of less than one node.

In this example the blocks were very similar. Indeed, the block mean square equals 1.82, which is less than that in the error line. There is nothing impossible about this; indeed, if the factors associated with blocks had no effect, both mean squares would measure the same sources of variation, and it would be a matter of chance which one proved to be larger. The smallness of the mean squared deviation for blocks is, however, noteworthy, because clearly no important sources of variation have been associated with blocks, so some have perhaps been left in error. However, the standard deviation of 2.887 is less than 5 per cent of the mean value, i.e., of 1509/24, and this is unusually small, so there is no call to modify techniques in further experiments. Perhaps such low coefficients of variation are usual with this sort of measurement—there does not appear to be a lot of published evidence about this—it is, however, clear that this experiment has proved to be gratifyingly precise and sensitive.

Sometimes when the variation associated with blocks is small, as here, the suggestion is made that it could well be pooled with error. In the actual experiment that gave the low value for the block mean square, it would be wrong to amend the analysis. If block variation is pooled with error whenever it is small and kept separate whenever it is large, the effect over a period will be to bias the estimates of error. As a proposal for future experiments, however, this suggestion may be very sensible. If the sources of variation associated with blocks have had no effect in the present experiment, there may be no need to bother about them in future ones; one-way classifications will then suffice. The decision can, however, be a rather difficult one. If blocks are omitted and one of the sources of variation does have an effect in certain circumstances, it will from time to time inflate the error and give rise to a poor experiment. Accordingly blocks are a useful insurance. The only disadvantage of using them is the reduction they bring about in the number of degrees of freedom for error, and this may be serious if the experiment is small. However, provided there are 12 to 15 degrees of freedom for error, little is gained by adding to them, so in larger experiments blocks are almost always used. A possible compromise is to use blocks containing two plots of each treatment or even three.

3.3   ORTHOGONAL THREE-WAY CLASSIFICATIONS

In 1782 the mathematician Euler gave a lecture to the Zeeland Scientific Society in Holland. He began by setting them a problem. The emperor, he said, was visiting a certain garrison town. Now there are six ranks of officers, and in this town there were six regiments, which gave the commandant the idea of taking 36 officers, one of each rank from each of the regiments, and disposing them in a square so that, whichever row or whichever file the emperor passed along, he would meet one officer of each rank and each regiment. Euler, being a mathematician, designated ranks by Latin letters, as he called them, and regiments by Greek ones. He managed his Latin square easily enough and proceeded to show that a Greek square could not be managed simultaneously. In this he was quite right, though his proof is unfortunately fallacious. Nevertheless, he gave a name to an important experimental design.

Latin squares have been used as experimental designs for a long time. Their first application was in agriculture, where it became the practice to divide a rectangular field into strips to form a series of blocks known as "rows," there being as many rows as treatments. The field was then divided into strips at right angles to the first set, these being known as columns, their number also being equal to that of the treatments. Finally, the treatments were allocated so that each occurred once in each row and once in each column. A Latin square gives a three-way classification of rows, columns, and treatments, such that each classification is orthogonal to both the others, as appears from the specimen in Table 3.6 (1). However,

Table 3.6
Examples of orthogonal three-way classifications

(1)	A	E	C	B	D	(2)	A	C	B	(3)	A	B	C	A	B
	D	B	A	C	E		B	A	C		C	A	A	B	B
	B	C	E	D	A		C	A	B		B	A	B	A	C
	E	D	B	A	C		B	C	A		A	C	B	B	A
	C	A	D	E	B		A	B	C		B	B	A	C	A
							C	B	A						

other orthogonal three-way classifications exist, as appears from Table 3.6 (2 and 3).

The original purpose in agriculture was to obtain better control of the variation arising from environmental factors. Often the attempt succeeded, but if treatments are numerous, the rows and columns become long and straggling, and two poor blocking systems can be less efficacious than one good one. However, many instances arise where two sets of blocks are needed. For example, a field experiment is to be conducted on a hillside and it is desirable to form blocks to remove the effect of altitude, because at the bottom of the hill soil is likely to be deeper than at the top, moisture to be greater, and exposure less. Suppose, however, that the prevailing wind blows along the slope rather than across it. Plainly blocks are needed up the hill also if effects of wind exposure are to be eliminated, so a three-way classification is called for.

Such designs are useful even though rows and columns are not spatial in character. Indeed, their chief use comes when one set of blocks represents time, and the other, pieces of equipment in short supply, because they then make possible experiments that would otherwise be quite impracticable. Thus, a research worker having five incubators and five treatments might on the first occasion allocate one treatment to each incubator. He then repeats the work, reallocating the treatments so that each is tried with a different incubator. If he uses five occasions in all, he can have a Latin square, with rows for occasions, and columns for pieces of apparatus, thus eliminating simultaneously two sources of variation that could not have been associated with the same set of blocks.

The situation would have been the same if there had been five assistants on five occasions. If, however, he had had five assistants and five pieces of apparatus, he could have kept one assistant to each piece, and their effects could have been eliminated together by one set of blocks.

Incidentally, there is nothing special about the number 5; Latin squares exist in all sizes. Also, as has been said, useful orthogonal three-way classifications exist apart from Latin squares.

A three-way classification having been selected, its randomization causes no difficulty. Any design satisfying the requirements is written down, the rows are permuted at random, and then the columns. Finally, the treatments are allocated at random to the letters. This last step is not essential, but it is the final safeguard against unconscious bias.[1] For example, if it is decided to use a 4 × 4 Latin square, any square is written down, e.g.,

$$
\begin{array}{cccc}
B & C & D & A \\
C & A & B & D \\
D & B & A & C \\
A & D & C & B
\end{array}
$$

[1] A longer procedure is given by Fisher and Yates, but this is not essential.

Permuting rows gives

$$
\begin{array}{cccc}
D & B & A & C \\
A & D & C & B \\
C & A & B & D \\
B & C & D & A
\end{array}
$$

Permuting columns gives

$$
\begin{array}{cccc}
C & B & D & A \\
B & D & A & C \\
D & A & C & B \\
A & C & B & D
\end{array}
$$

Only the allocation of treatments to letters remains.

For the analysis of variance five summation terms are required:

$T,$ a total term, derived from the data
$T_1,$ a row term, derived from the row totals
$T_2,$ a column term, derived from the column totals
$T_3,$ a treatment term, derived from the treatment totals
$T_0,$ a correction term, derived from the grand total

The analysis of variance may now be written as in Table 3.7.

Table 3.7
Analysis of variance for an orthogonal three-way classification

Source	df[1]	Sum of squares
Rows	$r - 1$	$T_1 - T_0$
Columns	$c - 1$	$T_2 - T_0$
Treatments	$t - 1$	$T_3 - T_0$
Error	$N - r - c - t + 2$	$T - T_1 - T_2 - T_3 + 2T_0$
Total	$N - 1$	$T - T_0$

[1] Here there are r rows, c columns, t treatments, and N plots.

The error line has here been obtained by difference, because error, by definition, comprises those sources of variation that have not been associated with the classifications. In practice, the given algebraic expressions would be used, the values for degrees of freedom and sums of squared deviations being added as a check.

For Latin squares, $r = c = t$, and $N = t^2$, so the number of degrees of freedom for error is $(t - 1)(t - 2)$. For an experiment of similar size in randomized blocks it would have been $(t - 1)^2$.

Because treatments are orthogonal to both rows and columns, the tests and estimates already described need no modification for use with these designs. The sequential test is not, however, available.

It is a mistake to suppose that designs with three classifications are necessarily better than those with two. If two rubbish dumps, rows and columns, can remove more irrelevant variation than one, the designs have evident advantages. Otherwise, their use is merely a sophisticated way of reducing the number of degrees of freedom available for error.

3.4   A NUMERICAL EXAMPLE OF LATIN SQUARE DATA

An experiment was carried out in order to find out how the time of cutting of a grass crop affected the total amount of dry matter in the hay. Five treatments were proposed. With treatments A, B, and C, crops were taken on June 24, July 15, and October 31. In treatment A, cutting took place also on three previous dates: in B on two and in C on one. With treatments D and E, cutting dates were not fixed by the calendar but related to the date of emergence of ears. (In D, at emergence itself and twenty-eight and seventy days after; in E, twenty-eight and eighty-four days after. In both D and E there was a final cutting on October 31.) The experiment was designed as a Latin square in order to eliminate differences within the site. The data are presented in Table 3.8; they represent grams of dry matter.

Table 3.8
Data for the experiment on cutting grass

C, 1937;	D, 1712;	A, 1985;	B, 2552;	E, 2979
B, 1519;	E, 3018;	C, 1772;	A, 1504;	D, 1395
E, 4007;	A, 2747;	D, 2300;	C, 2552;	B, 2138
D, 2020;	C, 2288;	B, 1886;	E, 4176;	A, 3084
A, 1767;	B, 2240;	E, 4079;	D, 1941;	C, 2686

It is usually advisable to express data to three significant figures, i.e., there should be three digits that can vary from one to the other. Thus, data could well be

1.413,   1.536,   1.440,   etc.

or   101.413,   101.536,   101.440,   etc.

Admittedly this rule has sometimes to be relaxed and usually little harm results, but it is wise to err if at all on the safe side. It was with this rule in mind that a recommendation was given to express summation terms, etc., to two decimal places beyond those arising from the act of squaring. However, here, rather than express all figures to the nearest 10 grams, the data will be kept as they are, but the usual two additional decimal places in the summation terms will be omitted. Either way the same number of decimal places will be obtained with about the same amount of labor, and the proposed method is obviously more accurate.

Totals are as follows:

Rows
    11 165,   9 208,   13 744,   13 454,   12 713
Columns
    11 250,   12 005,   12 022,   12 725,   12 282
Treatments
    A, 11 087; B, 10 335; C, 11 235; D, 9 368; E, 18 259

These figures are checked by noting that they all give the same grand total, namely, 60 284.

The summation terms can now be evaluated:

Total (T)	160 332 378
Rows (T_1)	148 194 502
Columns (T_2)	145 596 832
Treatments (T_3)	155 421 905
Correction (T_0)	145 366 426

These lead to the analysis of variance in Table 3.9.

Table 3.9
Analysis of variance for the experiment on cutting grass

Source	df	Sum of squares	Mean square
Rows	4	2 828 076	
Columns	4	230 406	
Treatments	4	10 055 479	
Error	12	1 851 991	154 333
Total	24	14 965 952	

The standard deviation of the experiment is $\sqrt{154\,333} = 393$, which is about 16 per cent of the general mean, i.e., 2,411 grams per plot. For experiments of this sort such a coefficient of variation is not unusual.

The interpretation of any analysis must depend upon the questions being asked. Here, one question concerns treatments A, B, and C, which differ in having respectively three, two, and one earlier cuttings. Plainly, it would be of interest to take the extremes and see if there is evidence of their differing. The means are A, 2,217, and C, 2,247. The significance of this difference is given by

$$t = \frac{2\,247 - 2\,217}{\sqrt{\frac{2}{5}(154\,333)}} = \frac{30}{248} = 0.12$$

a value that has 12 error degrees of freedom and will be exceeded by chance on about nine occasions out of ten. Consequently, no importance need be attached to the difference. Actually, treatment B lies a little apart from A and C, but it is hard to suppose that two cuttings are bad compared with one or three. Also, the difference of the mean of $B(2,067)$ from the mean of A and C taken together (2,232) is still far from significance, as is shown by t being equal to

$$\frac{2\,232 - 2\,067}{\sqrt{(\frac{1}{5} + \frac{1}{10})154\,333}} = \frac{165}{215} = 0.77$$

In fact, on the evidence of this experiment it does not appear to matter how many earlier cuttings are made. Treatments D and E, on the other hand, are clearly different, t being equal to 7.17, a figure that would arise by chance much less often than once in a thousand times.

Further, E appeared to be better than the group A, B, C, because t equals

$$\frac{3652 - 2177}{\sqrt{(\frac{1}{5} + \frac{1}{15})154\,333}} = 7.27$$

The results have been presented in grams per plot; it would be better to convert them to kilograms per hectare or pounds per acre. This conversion could have been applied to the data before analysis, but there would then have been 25 calculations to make, so it is easier to apply it afterwards.

It may be asked in what respect this interpretation differs from applying a multiple-range test, since each ends in establishing groups. Here, however, only certain possible groupings are investigated, the nature of the treatments being taken into account. In a multiple-range test the treatments are regarded as an amorphous set, one grouping being as reasonable as any other. This is less sensitive and leads to results that are to some extent arbitrary.

3.5   GRAECO-LATIN SQUARES

Although Euler's problem has no solution, it is possible to form Graeco-Latin squares of other sizes, e.g.,

$A\alpha$ $B\gamma$ $C\delta$ $D\beta$
$D\gamma$ $C\alpha$ $B\beta$ $A\delta$
$B\delta$ $A\beta$ $D\alpha$ $C\gamma$
$C\beta$ $D\delta$ $A\gamma$ $B\alpha$

Here there are four classifications: rows, columns, Roman letters, and Greek letters; the last represent the treatments, and the others are available for unwanted variation. Any one of them is orthogonal to any other. However, few families require three rubbish dumps, and Graeco-Latin squares

Table 3.10
Analysis of variance for a Graeco-Latin square

Source	df	Sum of squares
Rows	$k-1$	$T_1 - T_0$
Columns	$k-1$	$T_2 - T_0$
Roman letters	$k-1$	$T_3 - T_0$
Treatments	$k-1$	$T_4 - T_0$
Error	$(k-1)(k-3)$	$T - T_1 - T_2 - T_3 - T_4 + 3T_0$
Total	$k^2 - 1$	$T - T_0$

are rare. Where they do appear, it is often because a previous experiment in Latin squares has been finished and the material is still available for a further experiment. If it can be assumed that the effect of the new treatments (Greek letters) will be unaffected by the former treatments (Roman letters), a Graeco-Latin square may be ideal. Six summation terms are required: T, from the data; T_1, T_2, T_3, and T_4, respectively, from the row, column, Roman letter, and treatment totals; and T_0 from the grand total. The analysis then reads as in Table 3.10, k being the number of rows, columns, etc. Generalization to any four-way orthogonal classification is quite easy. The expressions in the error line can usefully be noted. For any orthogonal design the error sum of squares always equals T *minus* all the classification terms *plus* the correction term as many times as are needed to ensure that the same number of terms have been added as subtracted. Also, for k replicates, each of k treatments, the error degrees of freedom are $(k-1)(k-c+1)$ where c is the number of orthogonal classifications.

3.6   MULTIPLE LATIN SQUARES

One difficulty with Latin squares is their inflexibility in respect to replication; each treatment must have as many plots as there are treatments. The best way of overcoming this weakness is to use several Latin squares at once, and this can be done in several ways. For example, two squares can be taken and randomized thus:

$$
\begin{array}{ccc\quad ccc}
A & B & C & \quad C & B & A \\
C & A & B & \quad A & C & B \\
B & C & A & \quad B & A & C
\end{array}
$$

and then the columns can be permuted at random to form, say, this design:

$$
\begin{array}{cccccc}
B & A & C & A & C & B \\
C & C & B & B & A & A \\
A & B & A & C & B & C
\end{array}
$$

in which the first, fourth, and fifth columns come from one square, and the second, third, and sixth from the other. Such a design is a straightforward three-way classification; in it the Latin squares are said to be "tied."

Sometimes it is thought better to keep the squares separate, either because it is physically not possible for the same rows to run through all squares or because it is thought that more variation can be discarded in several sets of short rows than in one set of long. If the squares are not tied, the special feature of the analysis arises from the rows and columns lying within the squares and not within the experiment as a whole. Six summation terms are needed:

T,   from the data
T_1,   from the row totals
T_2,   from the column totals
T_3,   from the treatment totals
T_s,   from the square totals
T_0,   from the grand total

The analysis of variance has the form shown in Table 3.11, there being $n\,k \times k$ squares.

Table 3.11
Analysis of variance for multiple untied Latin squares

Source	df	Sum of squares
Squares	$n - 1$	$T_s - T_0$
Rows within squares	$n(k - 1)$	$T_1 - T_s$
Columns within squares	$n(k - 1)$	$T_2 - T_s$
Treatments[1]	$k - 1$	$T_3 - T_0$
Error	$(k - 1)(nk - n + 1)$	$T - T_1 - T_2 - T_3 + T_s + T_0$
Total	$nk^2 - 1$	$T - T_0$

[1] Treatments are orthogonal to rows, columns, and squares, so all the usual tests and estimates can be used without modification.

CHAPTER FOUR

AN EXAMINATION
OF ASSUMPTIONS

THE ASSUMPTIONS IMPLICIT IN THE ANALYSIS
OF VARIANCE AND HOW THEY CAN OFTEN BE
MET BY "TRANSFORMING" THE DATA. SUCH
TRANSFORMATIONS ARE SOMETIMES
BIOLOGICALLY MEANINGFUL AND CAN BE A
HELP IN INTERPRETATION.

THOSE WHO MAINTAIN THAT EVERYTHING IS WELL SPEAK
FOOLISHLY; THEY SHOULD SAY THAT EVERYTHING IS FOR THE
BEST. VOLTAIRE "CANDIDE" CHAPTER I

In the preceding chapters a number of arithmetical processes
have been described and their validity discussed in relation to the most important consideration of all, namely, their appropriateness to the problem
under study. Nevertheless, certain other assumptions have been implicit,
both about the design of the experiment and the behavior of the data. These
will now be examined.

4.1 RANDOMIZATION

Randomization has already been briefly mentioned; it enters into the
validity of an experiment in several ways. Thus, the experimental plants
or animals should in general be a random selection of those available. It
may be very reasonable to exclude chlorotic plants from a fertilizer trial,
provided it is understood that the results will refer only to normal plants.
It may be equally reasonable, if an excess of plants remains, to exclude those
that are very small or very large, as long as it is understood that the standard
deviation found is not representative of the complete population. If, however, it is desired to obtain results that can be applied to a general class of
plants or animals, the material used should as far as possible be a random
selection of the class.

Further, the material allocated to each treatment must be a random
selection of that used in the experiment as a whole. Whether the experiment
is intended to test or to estimate, there must be no biasing of treatment
means by unfair selection. (It is said that a large experiment on the effects of
supplementary food for school children in a poor district was vitiated
because the selection of the children had been left to the teachers, who
sometimes contrived that sickly children should receive the best supple-
ment.) If a treatment really does have certain effects, it must be shown to do
so on representative material, not just on material selected for it.

There is, however, another reason for randomizing, namely, the need to obtain an unbiased estimate of the error. Suppose, for example, that a botanist is growing tomato plants in pots on a bench in a greenhouse. It would be so much easier for him if he could have all plants of treatment A together, then all plants of treatment B, and so on, but he recognizes that if he does, he cannot separate treatments from positional effects on the bench. Accordingly, he proposes instead to arrange everything systematically, with treatments in the same order, A, B, C, etc., in each block. It is, however, pointed out to him that this always places treatment A at the same end of each block, and any trend along the bench, which ought to be associated with error, will in fact come out as treatments. He sees the reason of this and proposes instead to reverse the order in each block, starting with A in blocks I, III, etc., and ending with it in blocks II, IV, etc., but this still will not do. He is now preventing the error from entering into the treatment comparisons. Hence the treatment variation will be underestimated and the error, which is obtained by difference, will be overestimated. This means that it will be more difficult to establish the significance of differences. The only safe course is for him to assign his treatments at random in each block, troublesome though this may be.

This does not mean that important sources of variation should be allocated to the various plots by a random process and so appear as error. It is much better to associate them with a blocking system. Equally, it is quite wrong to meddle with the randomizations so that they are balanced out among the treatments, because, as has been explained, this inflates the error of the analysis.

Indeed, it is much better never to meddle with the randomization for any reason. This may seem a rather extreme position considering how very systematic some randomizations can be. Also, it is true that most people have at some time turned to a fresh page of random numbers after producing a design in which one half is identical with the other, is the mirror image of it, or in which some other pronounced regularity has arisen. Nevertheless, such occasions should be very few. Of course, it is always wrong to meddle with the randomization in order to put a chosen treatment on the best plots.

4.2 REPLICATION

The number of plots assigned to a treatment is said to be its degree of replication. Plainly, no analysis of variance is possible if treatments are so poorly replicated that there are no error degrees of freedom; indeed, no very satisfactory experiment is possible unless there are 12 to 15 degrees of freedom for error. Also, increased replication leads to a reduction in the standard error of a treatment mean, though it is a laborious business to achieve accuracy by replication alone. To halve the standard error it is necessary to use four times the degree of replication; to reduce it to a tenth, the replication must be increased to a hundred times what it was before, so the investigator who is told that his experiment with six replicates is not large enough does little good by deciding next time to use eight replicates instead. Much the best way of improving experimental accuracy is to identify sources of error, so as either to remove them or to associate them with the blocks.

4.3   HOMOGENEITY OF ERROR

So far the error has been spoken of as if all plots were equally subject to it, but this is not necessarily so. Thus, in the pear-grafting experiment the error sum of squared deviations was made up of three components, one from each of the varieties, but some varieties may be affected by factors that do not operate on any others.

In a one-way classification this is easily tested because there is no difficulty in isolating the components. Thus in the pear-grafting experiment the sums of squares are

> 10 323 with 3 degrees of freedom, mean square $= 3441$
> 19 809 with 6 degrees of freedom, mean square $= 3302$
> and   26 459 with 5 degrees of freedom, mean square $= 5292$

Bartlett has proposed a test of the homogeneity of these components. (It will be noticed that the decimal places of the sums of squares have been omitted. Usually they would be required, but here variability is so large that they add very little.) The first task is to work out mean squared deviations for the components separately and as a group and then to take logarithms, thus:

	Mean square	log (Mean square)
Separately	3441	3.5367
	3302	3.5188
	5292	3.7236
As a group	4042	3.6066

Then each value in the second column is multiplied by its degrees of freedom, products formed above the line being subtracted from the one below, i.e.,

$$(14 \times 3.6066) - (3 \times 3.5367) - (6 \times 3.5188) - (5 \times 3.7236)$$
$$= 0.1515$$

If it happened that each component had given exactly the same mean square, this quantity would have been zero. In practice it never is, and Bartlett's test enables a judgment to be made whether or not the value just found is too large for a homogeneous error.

The next task is to work out reciprocals of the numbers of degrees of freedom, again taking a difference between the values above the line and that below, i.e.,

$$\tfrac{1}{3} + \tfrac{1}{6} + \tfrac{1}{5} - \tfrac{1}{14} = \tfrac{132}{210} = H$$

The next quantity to be calculated is

$$0.4343 \left(1 + \frac{H}{3(k-1)}\right)$$

where k is the number of components. In this instance it equals 0.480. The final figure is $0.1515/0.480 = 0.316$, which is referred to χ^2 tables (Table IV of Fisher and Yates) with $(k-1)$ degrees of freedom. It appears that P is approximately 0.85, so there is no question of the mean squares from the three components being significantly different; indeed, they are rather similar.

With a two-way classification it is rather more difficult to divide the error into components, but heterogeneity of error still has to be watched for. Thus, W. G. Cochran[1] discusses an example in which an experimenter counted the poppies in plots of oats and obtained the figures shown in Table 4.1.

Table 4.1
Poppy counts in plots of oats

Block	Treatment					
	A	B	C	D	E	F
I	538	438	77	115	17	18
II	422	442	61	57	31	26
III	377	319	157	100	87	77
IV	315	380	52	45	16	20

[1] W. G. Cochran, *Empire Journal of Experimental Agriculture*, 6:158.

He very justly remarks that the results "are fairly clear on inspection," but points out that an analysis of variance does not show a significant difference ($P = 0.05$) between treatments C or D on the one hand and E or F on the other. He explains that there is much greater variation in treatments A and B than in the others, and this is included in the error line. The resulting mean square is then treated as if it referred to all treatments equally.

The problem is to partition the error sum of squares (39 799 with 15 degrees of freedom) into components that can be submitted to Bartlett's test, and to make the partition in some objective manner. One suggestion is to regard the one experiment as if it were three—one with treatments A and B, another with C and D, and a third with E and F. (The groups have been formed on the basis of the treatment means, not on the apparent variabilities.) These subexperiments have error sums of squares, each with 3 degrees of freedom, of 8,328.4, 4,645.5, and 58.5. Applying Bartlett's test gives 9.38 with 2 degrees of freedom, and this is highly significant ($P < 0.01$), so here there is clear evidence of heterogeneity of error. It will be noticed that only 9 of the 15 degrees of freedom for error have been dealt with, but this does not invalidate the argument.

The remedies for heterogeneity will be considered later. For the moment it suffices to note that analyses of variance, to be valid, require errors to be homogeneous.

4.4   ADDITIVITY

Another assumption that is implicit in the foregoing chapters is that of additivity. When discussing orthogonality, the point was made that if each treatment occurs equally often in each block, differences between blocks will not affect the comparison of treatment means. This would not be true, however, if the treatments had different effects in different blocks, as would be the case in a nutritional experiment where some blocks were made up of animals with a history of poor feeding. Not only would these animals grow less, but the differences between treatments might be much greater than in blocks of animals previously well fed. Again, an investigation into the relative efficacy of different prophylactic measures might run into similar difficulty if some blocks were made up of aggressively healthy persons who were unlikely to contract the disease anyway and other blocks contained persons who might be especially susceptible.

What is being assumed, really, is that the response of a plot is the straightforward sum of (1) a block effect, which would be the same for any other treatment, (2) a treatment effect, which would be the same in any other block, and (3) a residual effect, which arises solely from the operation of factors left in error and does not depend upon either blocks or treatments.

The best way of looking for nonadditivity is to work out the "residual" for each plot and to see if it does appear to be related to blocks or treatments, or, in a three-way classification, to rows, columns, or treatments.

In an orthogonal design the residual is best worked out by considering the formula for evaluating the error sum of squared deviations. For a two-way classification it is

$$T - T_1 - T_2 + T_0$$

where the summation terms relate respectively to data, block means, treatment means, and general mean. The residual for any plot equals (datum) − (block mean) − (treatment mean) + (general mean). Thus, in the pea growth-substance trial the residuals are as shown in Table 4.2. They should

Table 4.2
Residuals in the pea growth-substance trial (Data in Table 3.3)

	Block			
	I	II	III	IV
Untreated control	−0.37	+0.46	+0.30	−0.37
Gibberellic acid	−0.37	−1.54	+2.30	−0.37
Kinetin	+2.13	−1.04	−0.20	−0.87
Indole acetic acid	+0.63	+2.46	−0.70	−2.37
Adenine sulphate	−0.87	+0.96	−1.20	+1.13
Maleic hydrazide	−1.12	−1.29	−0.45	+2.88

add to zero for each block and each treatment. Also, if squared and added, they should give the error sum of squares, and this figure, 43.29, is very close to that found previously. The residuals have not, however, been worked out in order to check the error line, but in order to scrutinize the operation of error, which, it appears, does arise fairly evenly in all blocks and all treatments, except perhaps in the untreated control. Since the purpose of the experiment is to compare each of the other treatments with the control, and since the control is perhaps better estimated than was supposed, this information enhances confidence rather than weakens it.

It might be thought that calculation of the residuals should also show up heterogeneity of error. In the poppy data, for example, the residuals are as shown in Table 4.3.

Table 4.3
Residuals in oats experiment (Data in Table 4.1)

Block	Treatment					
	A	B	C	D	E	F
I	+99.0	+17.2	−35.8	+9.7	−46.8	−43.3
II	+10.3	+48.5	−24.5	−21.0	−5.5	−8.0
III	−47.7	−87.5	+58.5	+9.0	+37.5	+30.0
IV	−61.5	+21.7	+1.7	+2.2	+14.7	+21.2

However, this is not a good method, because an extreme value affects the treatment and block means relating to the plot and can give rise to quite large residuals in other plots of the same block and treatment. Nevertheless, in this example, the three largest residuals are in fact from treatments A and B.

Methods have been suggested for testing nonadditivity, and these are often useful. However, in a sense, all error arises from some form or other of nonadditivity, so if a test is to do more than establish the existence of error, it must postulate some pattern of nonadditivity and test that. There can therefore be no test for nonadditivity in general.

4.5   DISCONTINUITY

It has also been assumed that quantities are measured on a continuous scale. It is true that in practice they are taken to the nearest millimeter or the nearest kilogram or whatever the unit may be, but the unit of measurement should not exceed one-tenth of the total range encountered in the experiment. (Incidentally, this ideal was not quite achieved in the pea growth-substance experiment.) It is therefore wrong to try to use the analysis of variance with data such as those in Table 4.4.

It is not clear what method should be used, but the fault basically lies in the data themselves. Various suggestions might be made for improving future experiments. An obvious one is to measure more accurately. This would not be possible if the data represented subjective grades, but even here suggestions can be made. Thus, each plot might be graded by several observers and the results added. Alternatively, each plot might be divided into parts, each part graded separately, and the results added as before.

Table 4.4
Example of discontinuous data

Block	Treatment			
	A	B	C	D
I	0	0	0	1
II	0	2	0	1
III	1	1	1	0

4.6 TRANSFORMATIONS

Difficulties sometimes result from a wrong scale of measurement. Thus the areas of lesions caused by fungal infection are often unsatisfactory as data because they both give rise to a heterogeneous error and show evidence of nonadditivity. If, however, the square roots of the data are used instead, these troubles will often disappear. If this were just a statistical stratagem without biological meaning, it would rightly be regarded with some suspicion, but the lesions are now being measured by a quantity proportional to the radius, i.e., the distance of spread of the infection from the original spore, and this is immediately seen as good biological sense, because this could well be the quantity directly affected by both the treatments and the factors that make up error.

A similar case arises when studying the total weight of an animal or plant, where it often happens that the logarithm of weight gives a better variate than the weight itself; this is frequently true of any size record. Again, the transformation has drawn attention to something more fundamental than the quantity actually measured, namely, the growth rate. A change of nutrition or of health does not immediately make the test subjects larger or smaller, but it may well lead to a change in the rate at which they are growing.

These two transformations, the square-root and the logarithmic, are quite commonly met. Statistically speaking, the one corresponds to the case where the standard deviation of a plot varies with the square root of the plot value, and the other to the case where it varies proportionately with it.

Before proceeding, mention should be made of yet a third possibility, namely, the angular transformation, which is often used with proportions. Thus, suppose that each plot contains the same number of distinct units, whether it be insects or fruits or roots or anything else. In each plot a record is made of the proportion dead or diseased or growing or possessing any other recognizable character. The proportions will often not be suitable for study by the analysis of variance, because extreme values near 0 or 100 per cent will be less variable than those around 50 per cent, and a heterogeneous error will result. In such circumstances it is usual to transform to "angles of equal information" (Fisher and Yates, Tables XII and XIII), i.e., to the angle θ, where $(\sin \theta)^2$ equals the proportion. Thus 50 per cent transforms to $45°$ because $\sin 45 = \sqrt{\frac{1}{2}}$, so $(\sin 45)^2 = \frac{1}{2} = 50$ per cent. In this instance the transformation is being recommended for a statistical reason and not for a biological one. There is indeed no suggestion that the transformed variate has any biological meaning at all, certainly not that its meaning is more fundamental than that of the untransformed. Also, the transformation may lead to a homogeneous error, but it may also be a cause rather than a cure of nonadditivity. If most of the percentages lie in the range 15 to 85, i.e., there are no extreme values, little is gained by the transformation, and the data may be left as they are.

It should not be supposed that angles of equal information are suitable for all percentages and proportions. Thus, some percentage records are not bounded by 0 and 100. This is so when the number of fruit on a plant is expressed as a percentage of the number of blossom trusses, because with many species there can be more than one fruit from a single truss. Also, it often happens that the number of units varies considerably from plot to plot. For example, in an experiment on the control of a fungal disease, the number of spores in a standard sample might be counted and a record made of the proportion to germinate. With some treatments there may be more spores in a sample than with others, this leading to better estimation of the proportion, but the transformation will take no account of this. The best course, if possible, is to base the proportion of germinated spores on a constant number; this might save work by eliminating unnecessary counting, or it might lead to a sampling procedure of forbidding complexity. Everything depends on the circumstances.

4.7   STATISTICAL ARGUMENTS
FOR TRANSFORMATION

The sort of statistical reasoning that leads to the use of angles of equal information can also lead to a square-root transformation. If an unlikely event is given many chances of happening, the resulting distribution of occurrences will lead to an error far from homogeneous. For example, samples of leaves may be taken and a certain species of insect counted for each sample. The probability that any particular insect in the neighborhood will alight on a sample leaf just before it is picked is infinitesimally small; on the other hand, there may be very many insects. Similar cases often arise where the data represent a count of an unlikely occurrence given many chances to happen. In such circumstances a square-root transformation can be very helpful.

However, even here a careful consideration of the biological situation is needed. Thus, in a migration period the square-root transformation may be the one needed; on the other hand, after a period when insect populations have been increasing without migration, the number in a sample might be chiefly determined by the rate of increase, and a logarithmic transformation would be better. Further, to complicate the situation, control measures may have different effects on the distribution of counts. Thus, the introduction of predators will usually lead to a reduction of population where it is most dense, thus reducing extreme values, but the use of toxic sprays may lead to foci of infestation in sheltered places where the spray cannot reach, i.e., giving rise to extreme values.

In fact, the position is too complicated for dogmatism. An experimenter who grasps this simple fact and who realizes also that no transformation is used because it is perfect, but only because it is better than no transformation at all, will save himself a lot of anxiety. In practice, most people decide the matter by a method so crude as to seem absurd, but in the main it is effective. They note in each treatment the mean and the range, i.e., the difference between the extreme values. Thus, in the poppy data the treatment means are respectively 413, 395, 87, 79, 38, and 35. The corresponding ranges are 223, 119, 105, 70, 71, and 59. For the logarithmic transformation to be appropriate, the range and the mean should be proportionate, but this is not true here; the means of treatments A and B are over ten times those of E and F, whereas their ranges are only three or four times as great. For a square-root transformation, the ranges should increase as the square root of the means, as happens more or less here, $\sqrt{10}$ being about 3.2. The method can be vitiated by very large differences between blocks and is most effective when each treatment has four to six replicates. Also, an experimenter with large experience of a particular kind of data commonly develops soundly based practices that are independent of the particular set of data before him.

A square-root transformation for the poppy data seems reasonable on statistical grounds also, because the germination of a seed in circumstances where farming practice aims at preventing it is another instance of the unlikely event given many chances of happening.

4.8 PRESENTATION OF RESULTS USING TRANSFORMATIONS

The chief objection to transformation often lies in a suspicion that the results will defy either interpretation or presentation. However, this difficulty is not insuperable, as the poppy data show. Using a square-root transformation, the data become those in Table 4.5. The residuals are now very much better than those without transformation.

Table 4.5
Data of Table 4.1 after square-root transformation

Block	Treatment						
	A	B	C	D	E	F	
I	23.2	20.9	8.8	10.7	4.1	4.2	71.9
II	20.5	21.0	7.8	7.5	5.6	5.1	67.5
III	19.4	17.9	12.5	10.0	9.3	8.8	77.9
IV	17.7	19.5	7.2	6.7	4.0	4.5	59.6
	80.8	79.3	36.3	34.9	23.0	22.6	276.9
	In this form the residuals are:						
I	+2.6	+0.6	−0.7	+1.5	−2.1	−1.9	
II	+0.6	+1.5	−1.0	−0.9	+0.1	−0.3	
III	−2.2	−3.4	+2.0	−0.2	+2.1	+1.7	
IV	−0.9	+1.3	−0.3	−0.4	−0.1	+0.5	

The next task is to work out the summation terms, as follows:

Total	4180·6100
Blocks	3224·4050
Treatments	4098·1475
Correction	3194·7338

It would be expected that the total summation term in this analysis would equal the total of the original data (4,187). (All that has happened is the taking of the square roots and the squaring of them again.) Rounding-off errors have, however, prevented precise agreement.

From these summation terms it appears that the full analysis of variance is that in Table 4.6.

Table 4.6
Analysis of variance for the data in Table 4.5

Source	df	Sum of squares	Mean square
Blocks	3	29.6712	
Treatments	5	903.4137	
Error	15	52.7913	3.5194
Total	23	985.8762	

It is not clear from the original paper what experimental situation gave rise to these data; consequently it cannot be known what use should be made of the analysis just obtained. However, for purposes of demonstration this is something of an advantage because several techniques can be illustrated.

If an F test were required, it could be carried out as for any other analysis. Techniques that involve treatment means, however, run into an immediate difficulty, for if means of the transformed variate are taken, i.e.,

$$A \quad B \quad C \quad D \quad E \quad F$$
$$20.20 \quad 19.83 \quad 9.08 \quad 8.73 \quad 5.75 \quad 5.65$$

they are of themselves meaningless, because no one thinks naturally in terms of the square root of poppy counts. Accordingly, they should be squared to restore the original scale of measurement, namely,

$$A \quad B \quad C \quad D \quad E \quad F$$
$$408.0 \quad 393.2 \quad 82.4 \quad 76.2 \quad 33.1 \quad 31.9$$

This process is called "back transformation." It now appears that the back-transformed means are less than those that arise from the original data, namely,

$$A \quad B \quad C \quad D \quad E \quad F$$
$$413.0 \quad 394.8 \quad 86.8 \quad 79.3 \quad 37.8 \quad 35.3$$

However, this shift is a result of less weight being given in the back-transformed figures to the occasional high values thrown up in the untransformed data; it is therefore reasonable. With angles of equal information the shift is away from 50 per cent toward 0 or 100. Usually the best procedure is to work with the transformed figures but to express the result in terms of the back-transformed. Though not ideal, it is a good deal better than any alternative. Thus, if it is a question of finding confidence limits $(P = 0.05)$ for the mean of treatment A, these are

$$20.20 \pm 2.131 \sqrt{3.5194/4} = 20.20 \pm 2.00$$

i.e., 18.20 and 22.20. The results are therefore expressed by estimating the mean as $408.0(= 20.20^2)$ with confidence limits $(P = 0.05)$ of

$$331.2(= 18.20^2)$$

and $492.8(= 22.20^2)$. The fact that the confidence limits extend more in the upward direction than in the lower again reflects a tendency in the original data for a mean to arise from a few very high values balanced by a larger number of low ones.

Again, if it is a question of the significance of the difference between the means of treatments D and F, this is worked out on the transformed values, i.e.,

$$t = \frac{8.73 - 5.65}{\sqrt{2 \times 3.5194/4}} = 2.32$$

a value of t that must be judged significant at the level $P = 0.05$, this result being applied to the back-transformed values, 76.2 and 31.9.

The logarithmic transformation has an especially useful property: a constant change in the transformed variate corresponds to a constant ratio in the back-transformed. Let $\log R = D$. Then, if two means on the transformed scale would be considered to be significantly different if they were more than D apart, the means on the back-transformed scale differ significantly if one is more than R times the other. Similarly, if in the transformed scale confidence limits can be found by adding or subtracting D, in the back-transformed scale they can be found by multiplying or dividing by R. This greatly facilitates the presentation of results.

4.9 THE TRANSFORMATION OF DISCONTINUOUS VARIATES

In transforming data, discontinuity can be especially difficult. With the untransformed data the steps, though large, will at least be even; when transformed, the steps are still large but no longer all the same. Thus, if counts are made of a species of plant found in quadrats, the possible values are 0, 1, 2, 3, etc., but after a square-root transformation they are 0.00, 1.00, 1.41, 1.73, etc., values that are very difficult to deal with. A number of attempts have been made to help the situation by adding a constant to the variates before transformation, and there is general agreement that this is beneficial, though practice varies as to the constant to add. Almost any constant between 0 and 1 will effect an improvement, but the work of Anscombe shows the best value to be three-eighths. Thus, 0, 1, 2, 3, etc., become $\sqrt{\frac{3}{8}}$, $\sqrt{1\frac{3}{8}}$, $\sqrt{2\frac{3}{8}}$, $\sqrt{3\frac{3}{8}}$, etc., namely, 0.61, 1.17, 1.54, 1.84, etc., and a reasonable degree of homogeneity is achieved.

A similar device can be used with angles of equal information. If n units are observed, of which k have the character under study, the transformed variate θ should be taken so that

$$\sin^2 \theta = \frac{k + \frac{3}{8}}{n + \frac{3}{4}}$$

A logarithmic transformation is sometimes difficult to deal with because log 0 equals minus infinity. Strictly speaking, where this transformation is indicated, zero values should not arise, for it is impossible to have a plant or animal of zero size. However, if the quantity under study is really on a logarithmic scale, e.g., 1, $\frac{1}{2}$, $\frac{1}{4}$, $\frac{1}{8}$, etc., there comes a point when it will be measured as zero even though this is not strictly correct. Where discontinuity exists, log $(x + \frac{3}{8})$ is better than log x, and this avoids having to work with log 0. Nevertheless, an experimenter who finds himself with zeros in such data should satisfy himself that he is acting with good reason.

From what has been said it will be clear that transformations are often only expedients and that they are at best approximate in their action. This is not of itself a serious objection to their use. Untransformed data also rarely lead to perfectly homogeneous errors or to perfect additivity; this point may give some reassurance to the cautious. The greatest difficulties arise when it appears that one transformation will be best to obtain a homogeneous error, another will give additivity, and perhaps a third will give a simple relationship with another of the quantities under study. There is no rule for such instances; if the experimenter is aware of the situation, he will at least be able to avoid rash conclusions. Where a transformation has revealed a genuinely basic biological concept, however, such problems do not usually arise.

4.10   HIDDEN ASSUMPTIONS

However, the most dangerous assumptions are not the objective ones that are implicit in the technique and can therefore be listed; they are rather those implicit in the experimenter's mind, leading him to find only what he subconsciously expects. This is an ever-present danger. The task of science is to study phenomena so as to discern useful patterns and relationships; what is discerned reflects the working of the human mind as much as it does the phenomena observed.

This is a very old idea. It goes back to Kant and was held strongly by the physicist Eddington.[2] He argued that the human mind finds satisfaction in spatial patterns of similar objects, whereas in the face of qualitative differences it seeks a "deeper" explanation. Consequently, the description of the universe as a complex pattern of identical particles is the only one with which the mind can rest, and it is not surprising that the two kinds of particles accepted in his day, electrons and protons, were thought of as complementary. Further, their total number, to be satisfying, would have to contain as factors certain geometrical constants, and he pointed out that the product of these constants was in fact within observational limits of the estimated size of the universe. Thus, Eddington argued, the basic concepts of physics can be derived from the preconceptions of the human mind; whatever kind of universe presents itself, the ideas by which it is described will be the same.

Perhaps Eddington overstated his case, but it is no answer to say that physical concepts are more diversified than in his day. His contention was that scientific thinking is under pressure all the time to conform to certain models. Either human beings fail altogether to describe phenomena or they describe them in terms of a limited number of acceptable forms.

What bearing has this on the interpretation of biological data? On the wide front considered by Eddington it possibly has very little at the moment, but in specific cases his warning is important.

For example, experimenters are often told to look through their data before analyzing them, and this is most useful advice. It may appear that some are missing or are labeled ambiguously, and this enables faults to be rectified. Also, it may appear that the differences under study are too small to be important, and consequently it does not matter whether they are significant or not. Beyond this point danger creeps in.

For example, examination shows that some data lie apart from the rest,

[2] A. S. Eddington, "The Philosophy of Physical Science," Cambridge, 1939.

and these are investigated further in case they are wrong. If they are impossible, e.g., if 120 per cent of the seeds are alleged to have germinated, this is all very well, but if they are possible but divergent from the rest, there should be no hidden assumption that extreme values ought not to arise. With a range of treatments, the high values of high treatments can be expected to stand apart from the general body just as the low values of the treatment at the other end will do so. If these values are excluded, the effect will be to force all treatment means toward the middle, thus justifying the experimenter's preconceptions. He may retort that he is not excluding them, he is only checking them, but he does not check those in the middle in the hope of pushing them outwards. (Incidentally, the solution here is to examine the residuals, not the data themselves.)

Another danger to be avoided is that of testing a difference only because preliminary investigation shows it to be large. However, this has already been discussed in Chapter 2.

Preconceptions can enter in other ways. For example, a certain experimenter, who shall be nameless, applied a hormone to cuttings of a sort that usually will not root. Most of them died from an unidentified disorder, but two survived, both of which rooted, so he reported 100 per cent success. Subsequently the "kill or cure" nature of the treatment was recognized, but only after much time and energy had been expended. The original investigator had acted with complete honesty, but had failed to detect an assumption in his own mind. Everyone, authors and readers alike, need to be on their guard. Elaborate statistical techniques do nothing to give protection; indeed, they can obscure what would otherwise be obvious. Besides, the statistician also makes assumptions, as this chapter shows. Perhaps the most important aspect of collaboration between biologist and statistician is their ability to examine one another's preconceptions to the advantage of both.

CHAPTER FIVE

ANALYSIS OF VARIANCE FOR AN ARBITRARY DESIGN

EVEN IF THE DESIGNS OF CHAPTER 3 HAVE

NOT BEEN USED, IT IS OFTEN STILL POSSIBLE

TO USE THE ANALYSIS OF VARIANCE.

5.1   SOME BASIC IDEAS IN THE ANALYSIS
OF VARIANCE

In Chapter 3 the analysis of variance was considered with special reference
to a very useful and highly organized class of designs, namely, those called
"orthogonal." It should be said at once that these designs represent the
ideal, partly because they are simple to evolve and simple to analyze, and
partly because, in general, they extract maximum information from a given
number of observations. Nevertheless there are times when an experimenter
has to accept a design that is less than ideal. For example, suppose that there
are five treatments, which are to be studied using a species that usually
has four young to a litter. To obtain uniform material, it might be best
to use litters as blocks and animals as plots, but this presents difficulty
unless a sufficient number of litters of five can be obtained. If not, the
experimenter either has to make up blocks of similar animals from
different litters or abandon orthogonality of design. He might well prefer
the latter.

In doing so he might have to accept a heavy burden of computation,
but he need not fear that his experiment will be invalid. The conditions of
validity were set out in the last chapter, and they do not include orthogonality. In this chapter the analysis of variance will be considered in the
most general terms, without reference to any specific design at all.

This may seem a rather academic exercise, because few people experiment in conditions so difficult that they can bring no element of order at all
into their plans. Nevertheless, the exposition may elucidate what goes on in
an analysis of variance, and it may dispel fears about unusual designs.

For a start it will be best to go back to the analysis of variance for
orthogonal designs, because their very balance and symmetry has obscured
one important point, namely, the derivation of the treatment sum of squared
deviations. The logic of the method should be this. First of all, work out the
error sum of squared deviations, S, assuming that the treatments may have

had an effect. For an orthogonal two-way classification,

$$S = T - T_1 - T_2 + T_0$$

Now, suppose that one adopts the attitude of skepticism and asserts that the treatments cannot really have had any effect. In that case the design really has only one classification, that of blocks, and its sum of squared deviations for error is S', where

$$S' = T - T_1$$

The difference, $S' - S$, is attributed to treatments and equals $T_2 - T_0$, the expression already given for the treatment sum of squared deviations. With simple designs this looks obvious, but with more complex designs it is necessary to understand its derivation. Also, S has $(N - b - t + 1)$ degrees of freedom, S' has $(N - b)$, so $(S' - S)$ has $(t - 1)$. Again the result has already been used, but without considering its basis.

Also, in earlier chapters additivity has been mentioned without giving it algebraic form. What is really being implied in the whole statistical approach is that the data of an experiment represent the working of a natural mechanism, overlaid and obscured by the operation of error. The experimenter is regarded as seeking constants of nature, but never quite attaining their evaluation because he can never be certain how much of what he observes is error. These constants are called "parameters" and are conventionally represented by Greek letters; it is implied that any particular experimental observation comes from some function of the parameters

$$\alpha\beta + \gamma^2$$
or $$\alpha\beta\gamma + \delta\epsilon$$

with error added. An assertion of additivity implies that the functions of parameters lying behind the data, and thus giving shape and order to phenomena, consist solely of sums and differences, i.e.,

$$\alpha + \beta - \gamma$$
or $$\alpha - 2\beta + 3\gamma - \delta$$

and never more complicated ones like α^β or $\sqrt{\gamma}$.

At this point the biologist may understandably complain that statisticians appear to take a lot for granted, and may point out that many biological phenomena are too complicated to be expressed in such a way. However, the statistician, if he is wise, knows this too and will sometimes use transformations so that quite complicated relationships can be put into additive form. Nevertheless, a biologist ought to be aware of the statistician's tendency to think in these terms.

For purposes of experimental design, however, additivity is often a reasonable assumption. Let α be a general parameter representing the mean yield of wheat to be expected over the whole of the experimental area using an average variety; let β be a block parameter representing the difference from α for the block under study; and let γ be a treatment parameter representing the difference brought about by the variety actually sown. The assumption of additivity amounts to saying that the yield of that variety in that block should be

$$\alpha + \beta + \gamma + \text{error}$$

In effect, this means that varietal differences would not be altered by moving to another block and that block differences would be the same whichever variety was sown over the whole area. Such an assumption can hardly hold strictly, but it might well be a reasonable approximation to the facts.

5.2   A SIMPLE EXAMPLE OF AN ANALYSIS OF VARIANCE FOR AN UNSPECIFIED DESIGN[1]

In order to show how an analysis of variance can be carried out without placing any restrictions on the design of the experiment, the following fictitious set of data has been devised. Everything has been made as simple as possible—indeed, almost any genuine data would have called for much more arithmetic—but in principle any of the steps could be undertaken in any experiment. It should be admitted that many people manage very well without the knowledge that this section contains, but it is hoped that the reader will try to understand the method. It is true that he is most unlikely to use it in the stark form given here, but he will find out from it what is essential to an analysis of variance and what is not.

Suppose that there are four blocks, I to IV, and three treatments, A, B, and C, the data being as follows:

Block I: A, 14; B, 10; A, 13; C, 15
Block II: A, 13; C, 16
Block III: B, 11; A, 14; C, 14
Block IV: B, 10; C, 15

[1] From this point until the end of Chap. 6, the text contains more mathematics than elsewhere. Those allergic to the subject can start again at Chap. 7 without fear of being unable to pick up the thread.

Let there be a general parameter α, and let each block have its own parameter, β_1, β_2, β_3, and β_4, and let there be treatment parameters also, γ_A, γ_B, and γ_C. Then, for example, the value for treatment B in block IV should be

$\alpha + \beta_4 + \gamma_B +$ a component of error

First of all, the total for block I is 52. Adding parameters for its four plots shows that

$52 = 4\alpha + 4\beta_1 + 2\gamma_A + \gamma_B + \gamma_C +$ error

Similarly, from the other three blocks,

$29 = 2\alpha + 2\beta_2 + \gamma_A + \gamma_C +$ error
$39 = 3\alpha + 3\beta_3 + \gamma_A + \gamma_B + \gamma_C +$ error
$25 = 2\alpha + 2\beta_4 + \gamma_B + \gamma_C +$ error

Next, similar equations are derived from the totals for the three treatments, namely,

$54 = 4\alpha + 2\beta_1 + \beta_2 + \beta_3 + 4\gamma_A +$ error
$31 = 3\alpha + \beta_1 + \beta_3 + \beta_4 + 3\gamma_B +$ error
$60 = 4\alpha + \beta_1 + \beta_2 + \beta_3 + \beta_4 + 4\gamma_C +$ error

Finally there is the grand total, i.e.,

$145 = 11\alpha + 4\beta_1 + 2\beta_2 + 3\beta_3 + 2\beta_4 + 4\gamma_A + 3\gamma_B + 4\gamma_C +$ error

These are known as "normal equations." There are eight of them and eight parameters, so there would seem to be no obstacle to their solution except the hard work needed; but this is not so, because the last of them, that based on the grand total, could have been derived in two ways from the others, namely, by adding all those based on block totals or by adding all those based on treatment totals. In fact, no unique solution exists, and it is easy to see why. If a solution were found, someone else could add, say, 10 to α and subtract, say, 6 from all the values of β and then subtract 4 from all the values of γ and then assert with truth that the new values were as good a solution of the equations as the original ones, because all expressions of the form $\alpha + \beta + \gamma$ would be unchanged in value. To remove this indefiniteness, two equations need to be added. These are known as "equations of constraint" and can be purely conventional. A simple procedure is to make the block parameters and the treatment parameters sum to zero over the whole experiment, i.e., to make

$$4\beta_1 + 2\beta_2 + 3\beta_3 + 2\beta_4 = 0$$
$$4\gamma_A + 3\gamma_B + 4\gamma_C = 0$$

From this point there will be a change of notation. So far the Greek letters have represented ideal but unknown constants of nature, and "+ error" has had to be added to the right-hand side of several equations. From now on Greek letters will represent the best estimate that can be made of the parameters. Mathematicians have shown that these best estimates are found by disregarding error and just solving the equations. To be correct, from now on Greek letters should be differentiated by placing a circumflex or "hat" above them, but in this text, which makes no attempt to be mathematical, this refinement will be omitted.

By virtue of the equation of constraint,

$$145 = 11\alpha$$

i.e., the general parameter is estimated as the mean of the data or 13.182. The treatment parameters are best estimated by eliminating the block parameters, and this is very easily done. First the block totals are reduced to means, thus:

$$b_1 = 13.0 = \alpha + \beta_1 + \tfrac{1}{2}\gamma_A + \tfrac{1}{4}\gamma_B + \tfrac{1}{4}\gamma_C$$
$$b_2 = 14.5 = \alpha + \beta_2 + \tfrac{1}{2}\gamma_A + \tfrac{1}{2}\gamma_C$$
$$b_3 = 13.0 = \alpha + \beta_3 + \tfrac{1}{3}\gamma_A + \tfrac{1}{3}\gamma_B + \tfrac{1}{3}\gamma_C$$
and $$b_4 = 12.5 = \alpha + \beta_4 + \tfrac{1}{2}\gamma_B + \tfrac{1}{2}\gamma_C$$

Next, for each treatment a quantity Q is worked out by subtracting from the treatment total each block mean as often as the block contains the treatment, i.e.,

$$\begin{aligned}
Q_A &= 54 - 2b_1 - b_2 - b_3 \\
&= 54.0 - 26.0 - 14.5 - 13.0 \\
&= +0.5 \\
Q_B &= 31 - b_1 - b_3 - b_4 \\
&= 31.0 - 13.0 - 13.0 - 12.5 \\
&= -7.5 \\
\text{and}\quad Q_C &= 60 - b_1 - b_2 - b_3 - b_4 \\
&= 60.0 - 13.0 - 14.5 - 13.0 - 12.5 \\
&= +7.0
\end{aligned}$$

The values of Q always sum to zero, and this provides a useful check on the arithmetic. Their importance lies in their depending entirely on the treatment parameters. Thus,

$$Q_A = (4\alpha + 2\beta_1 + \beta_2 + \beta_3 + 4\gamma_A) - 2(\alpha + \beta_1 + \tfrac{1}{2}\gamma_A + \tfrac{1}{4}\gamma_B + \tfrac{1}{4}\gamma_C)$$
$$- (\alpha + \beta_2 + \tfrac{1}{2}\gamma_A + \tfrac{1}{2}\gamma_C)$$
$$- (\alpha + \beta_3 + \tfrac{1}{3}\gamma_A + \tfrac{1}{3}\gamma_B + \tfrac{1}{3}\gamma_C)$$
$$= (4 - 1 - \tfrac{1}{2} - \tfrac{1}{3})\gamma_A - (\tfrac{1}{2} + \tfrac{1}{3})\gamma_B - (\tfrac{1}{2} + \tfrac{1}{2} + \tfrac{1}{3})\gamma_C$$
$$= \tfrac{1}{12}(26\gamma_A - 10\gamma_B - 16\gamma_C)$$

Similarly,

$$Q_B = \tfrac{1}{12}(-10\gamma_A + 23\gamma_B - 13\gamma_C)$$

and $\quad Q_C = \tfrac{1}{12}(-16\gamma_A - 13\gamma_B + 29\gamma_C)$

These equations cannot be solved as they stand because they are not independent; any one of them can be derived by adding the other two and reversing signs. However, there is still the equation of constraint,

$$4\gamma_A + 3\gamma_B + 4\gamma_C = 0$$

Solution of the equations leads to the results

$$\gamma_A = +0.275$$
$$\gamma_B = -2.773$$
$$\gamma_C = +1.805$$

These are, of course, estimated values. Together with the estimate of α they provide quantities known as "adjusted treatment means" which represent the mean results per plot to be expected if a treatment is applied to the whole of the experimental area, namely,

$$A, \quad \alpha + \gamma_A = 13.457$$
$$B, \quad \alpha + \gamma_B = 10.409$$
$$C, \quad \alpha + \gamma_C = 14.987$$

Further, the treatment sum of squares, i.e., $S' - S$, can be found by multiplying each value of Q by the corresponding value of γ and adding. Here the result is

$$(0.5)(0.275) + (-7.5)(-2.773) + (7.0)(1.805) = 33.5700$$

Since S' is the error sum of squared deviations for the one-way classification that would result from ignoring treatments, it may readily be evaluated as a difference of two summation terms, as follows:

$$T = 14^2 + 10^2 + 13^2 + \cdots + 15^2 = 1\,953.00$$
$$T_1 = \frac{52^2}{4} + \frac{29^2}{2} + \frac{39^2}{3} + \frac{25^2}{2} = 1\,916.00$$

so $\quad S' = 1\,953.00 - 1\,916.00 = 37.00$

Since both $S'(= 37.00)$ and $(S' - S)(= 33.57)$ are now known, it is easy to evaluate S as $3.43 (= 37.00 - 33.57)$, this being the error sum of squared deviations. Also, the corresponding quantity for the block line of the analysis is found from the difference of two summation terms, T_1 and T_0, of which T_1 is already known and T_0 equals $145^2/11 = 1,911.36$. The sum of squared deviations for the total equals $T - T_0$, so the whole analysis can readily be completed as is done in Table 5.1.

Table 5.1
Analysis of variance for a nonorthogonal design

Source	df	Sum of squares	Mean square
Blocks	3	4.64	
Treatments	2	33.57	
Error	5	3.43	0.686
Total	10	41.64	

In this analysis the block line has been obtained exactly as if the design were orthogonal. Consequently no use should be made of it, except for providing a computational check of the total. The treatment and error lines, on the other hand, have been adjusted for blocks and are therefore valid; thus, an F test for treatments could justifiably be made, if needed. Also, though the methods will not be shown here, it is possible to find standard errors for adjusted treatment means and differences between them and thus to determine confidence limits and carry out t tests. In fact, despite the lack of organized design, an effective analysis of variance has been obtained. In the next chapter these results will be applied to designs that have some measure of organization without being as balanced as the orthogonal ones, but which, by their greater flexibility, allow for more freedom of approach in difficult conditions.

5.3 CHECKING OF COMPUTATIONS AND EVALUATION OF BLOCK PARAMETERS

The calculations in the last section have been complex, and ideally require checking. There are several ways of doing this, but the best require a prior evaluation of the block parameters.

In some circumstances this would need to be done anyway. Thus, one occasion for using nonorthogonal designs is the late appearance of differences that could not be identified earlier. For example, with some species it may be difficult to sex specimens at the start; this classification therefore cannot be controlled and will be orthogonal, if at all, only by good luck. In such an investigation the classification "sex," taking the place of the classification "block," may be as interesting as the classification "treatment."

The first check then is to "dualize," i.e., to change round the two classifications and to repeat the whole calculation reading "block" for "treatment" and "treatment" for "block." The check consists of getting the same error line as before, but this time the other valid line is that for blocks, while that for treatments should not be used further.

An alternative and shorter check is to find the block parameters from the expressions already given for block means. Thus,

$$13.0 = b_1 = \alpha + \beta_1 + \tfrac{1}{2}\alpha_A + \tfrac{1}{4}\gamma_B + \tfrac{1}{4}\gamma_C$$

Now that all other parameters are known it is a simple matter to turn the equation round and write

$$\beta_1 = 13.0 - \alpha - \tfrac{1}{2}\gamma_A - \tfrac{1}{4}\gamma_B - \tfrac{1}{4}\gamma_C$$
$$= -0.078$$

Similarly,

$$\beta_2 = 14.5 - \alpha - \tfrac{1}{2}\gamma_A - \tfrac{1}{2}\gamma_C$$
$$= +0.278$$
$$\beta_3 = 13.0 - \alpha - \tfrac{1}{3}\gamma_A - \tfrac{1}{3}\gamma_B - \tfrac{1}{3}\gamma_C$$
$$= +0.049$$
and $$\beta_4 = 12.5 - \alpha - \tfrac{1}{2}\gamma_B - \tfrac{1}{2}\gamma_C$$
$$= -0.198$$

These values may readily be checked by seeing if they satisfy the equation of constraint for blocks, i.e.,

$$4\beta_1 + 2\beta_2 + 3\beta_3 + 2\beta_4 = 0$$

In fact, the left-hand side gives -0.005, which is just satisfactory. (No value of β should be in error by more than 0.0005, and there are 11 values, so the highest conceivable deviation is 0.0055.)

It is now possible to obtain an independent check of the error sum of squared deviations. Each parameter should be multiplied by the total to which it refers, the products added, and their sum subtracted from the total summation term, T. In fact, S should equal

$$1\ 953.00 - 145(13.182) - 52(-0.078) - 29(0.278) - 39(0.049)$$
$$- 25(-0.198) - 54(0.275) - 31(-2.773) - 60(1.805) = 3.46$$

The check has worked out reasonably well. It will rarely prove perfect unless many more decimal places are carried in the calculations.

Once the block parameters are known, there is no difficulty in evaluating residuals. Thus the expected value for treatment B in block IV is

$$\alpha + \beta_4 + \gamma_B$$

which equals 10.211. Three significant places are enough, so this will be called 10.2. The actual value is 10, giving a residual of -0.2. Following this line of reasoning, the residuals are:

Block I: $A, +0.6$; $B, -0.3$; $A, -0.4$; $C, +0.1$
Block II: $A, -0.7$; $C, +0.7$;
Block III: $B, +0.5$; $A, +0.5$; $C, -1.0$
Block IV: $B, -0.2$; $C, +0.2$;

Naturally they sum to zero over each block and each treatment.

5.4   THREE-WAY NONORTHOGONAL CLASSIFICATIONS

So far nonorthogonality has been discussed solely as a relationship between two classifications. If there are three in an experiment, they can be formed into three pairs, 1 and 2, 1 and 3, and 2 and 3, and the relationship within each examined. It could be that all three are nonorthogonal, in which case the experimenter has a major task in hand if he is to analyze the data. To take a happier outcome, it might appear that two of the relationships are nonorthogonal and one orthogonal; the difficulties are now much reduced though the method of analysis will not be given here. If, however, only one of the relationships proves to be nonorthogonal, the outcome is happy indeed, because analysis is now scarcely more difficult than with two classifications.

The reason for this lies in there being one classification which is orthogonal to both the others. Consequently its sum of squared deviations can be evaluated as a difference of two summation terms. This classification is then ignored for a while, and attention concentrated on the diminished design consisting only of the other two. The data are analyzed as if only these classifications existed; then the degrees of freedom and sum of squared deviations for the third classification are extracted from the error and presented on a separate line, thus completing the analysis.

An early example of this by W. J. Youden remains a classic.[2] Youden was investigating the effects of viruses on tobacco plants and had two main sources of variation to avoid. One was that between plants, each one of which appeared to have its own characteristic susceptibility; the other was that between leaf positions, young leaves behaving differently from old ones. As long as there were only about five treatments, Latin squares provided an answer; but the time came when Youden needed seven concentrations each in three kinds of solution, or 21 treatments in all, and there was no chance of finding tobacco plants with 21 suitable leaves. The precise design is not stated in his paper, but the following reconstruction indicates his approach. He took 21 plants with five leaf positions on each and disposed his treatments according to the scheme in Table 5.2.

Table 5.2
Example of a "Youden square"

Position	Plant																				
	1	2	3	4	5	6	7	8	9	10	11	12	13	14	15	16	17	18	19	20	21
1	A	B	C	D	E	F	G	H	I	J	K	L	M	N	O	P	Q	R	S	T	U
2	B	N	U	O	F	H	K	S	P	E	M	T	Q	A	C	G	J	D	R	I	L
3	C	R	F	M	L	A	O	N	S	U	J	P	B	Q	I	E	G	H	T	K	D
4	D	F	K	T	S	G	B	M	J	O	A	H	I	P	L	R	C	Q	U	E	N
5	E	J	P	F	Q	I	S	C	D	H	L	B	U	O	R	M	T	K	A	N	G

It will be seen that:

1. Plants and leaf positions are orthogonal.
2. Treatments and leaf positions are orthogonal.
3. Treatments and plants are nonorthogonal.

However, as will appear later, the nonorthogonality is of a very regular kind. Since leaf positions are orthogonal to both the other classifications, their consideration can be postponed, leaving a diminished design with plants (used as blocks) and treatments, which can be analyzed as in Table 5.3.

[2] W. J. Youden, Estimating Tobacco-Mosaic Virus, *Contributions from Boyce Thompson Institute*, 9:41–48.

The classification by leaf position can now be treated as if the design were orthogonal, and will give a sum of squared deviations of, say, X. The full analysis is, therefore, that in Table 5.4.

Table 5.3
Analysis of variance for the diminished
design from Table 5.2

Source	df	Sum of squares
Plants	20	A
Treatments	20	B
Error	64	C
Total	104	A + B + C

Table 5.4
Analysis of variance for the full design from
Table 5.2

Source	df	Sum of squares
Plants	20	A
Leaf positions	4	X
Treatments	20	B
Error	60	C − X
Total	104	A + B + C

The line for plants was not valid in the analysis for the diminished design; it is not valid here, but everything else is.

Standard errors of adjusted treatment means and of differences between them are readily found. If "treatments" is the classification orthogonal to both the others, no adjustment is needed and standard errors are calculated as for an orthogonal design. If "treatments" is nonorthogonal to one of the others, everything is as for the diminished design except for the degrees of freedom and the mean squared deviation appropriate to error.

Residuals are readily calculated. For each level of the classification that is being ignored, a value is found representing the difference between the mean of the data for that level and the general mean of all data. Residuals are found for the diminished design, and then one of these values is subtracted according to the level of the ignored classification.

5.5   THE USES OF NONORTHOGONAL DESIGNS

As has been said, the great advantage of nonorthogonal designs lies in their greater flexibility, especially in the opportunity they provide for making use of a given block size or even for using blocks of different sizes. It is a feature of biological material that there is often a natural block—shoot, blossom truss, litter, or paired organs—each of which divides into natural plots—leaves, blossoms, animals, or individual organs. One of two difficulties usually appears. Either the number of plots to a block is constant, in which case the number is not necessarily ideal for the purpose in hand, or the number is variable, in which case very complicated designs are indicated. It is true that some plots can be discarded in either case, but this can be a very undesirable expedient if material is in short supply. Consequently, nonorthogonal designs can be especially useful in biological research.

The usual reason given for their adoption is that they enable use to be made of smaller blocks than those required by orthogonal designs. This is true, but in some fields of research small blocks are not better than large ones. The idea comes from field trials where the size of plots is determined chiefly by practical considerations, and consequently a reduction in the number of plots to a block implies a reduction in the area of a block and thus in the range of environmental conditions found in it, leading to a reduction in the error mean squared deviation. However, sound as this argument is in its original context, it does not apply in a field even as closely related as fruit research, where the performance of young apple trees is associated more with performance in the nursery than with conditions in the locations in which they are planted. (This is not true of their performance when mature, but some experiments are concerned solely with the first few years of orchard development.) In fields more remote the supposition may be true, but it should not be accepted without positive evidence.

The main objection to nonorthogonal designs is complexity, though this should not be overrated. There are designs that lack the extreme balance of orthogonality yet give data fairly easy to analyze. Another objection is loss of efficiency in estimating treatment means. Thus, in the example given in Section 5.3, the standard error of the difference between adjusted means of treatments A and C is $\sqrt{0.5543}$ error mean square. It is as if each had had 3.61 plots, because

$$\frac{1}{3.61} + \frac{1}{3.61} = 0.5543$$

In fact, each had four plots, so the efficiency is said to be 90.2 per cent, this being 3.61 expressed as a percentage of 4. (Of course, the value of the error mean square might be different in the orthogonal design because, if such a design were possible, the blocks would necessarily be different.)

In general, the more plots there are to a block in a nonorthogonal design, the higher the efficiency. On the other hand, the larger the block, the larger the error mean square is likely to be. The choice between large and small blocks is therefore a balancing of advantages, and no general rules can be given.

5.6   RANDOMIZATION OF NONORTHOGONAL DESIGNS

Throughout this book nonorthogonal designs will be written down in whatever form is clearest for illustrating the point to be made. This may give the impression that randomization is not required, but in fact it is essential whatever the design.

With an orthogonal two-way classification it is necessary within each block to allocate treatments to plots at random. With a nonorthogonal design, however, a special difficulty arises, because different groups of treatments need to be distributed among the blocks. Suppose, for example, that it is proposed to use a design in which one block takes B, C, and D; another, A, C, and D; a third, A, B, and D; and the last, A, B, and C. Which block takes which set? The strict answer is that the method of allocation is immaterial, but a sensible practice is to make it at random. Then, within each block the treatments assigned to it must be allocated to the plots; this must always be done randomly.

With a three-way classification the method is the same whatever the design, i.e., a possible plan is written down, the rows are permuted at random, and then the columns likewise.

CHAPTER SIX

ANALYSIS OF VARIANCE FOR SOME NONORTHOGONAL DESIGNS

SOME DESIGNS ARE DESCRIBED THAT LACK
THE RIGIDITY OF THOSE IN CHAPTER 3
BUT STILL HAVE A FAIR AMOUNT OF
ORGANIZATION. THESE FACILITATE
EXPERIMENTATION IN RESTRICTIVE
CONDITIONS.

Before leaving the subject of nonorthogonal designs, it will be as well to consider some of the more important classes. In general, even if orthogonality cannot be attained, it is still possible to devise a plan with enough regularity to simplify the computations and give a pattern to the accuracies with which the various pairs of treatments are compared.

6.1   DESIGNS OF TYPE T[1]

Suppose that a block contains five plots, with treatment A occurring twice and treatment B once. The treatments are said to have two (2×1) concurrences in that block. Dividing by the block size, 5, gives the "weighted concurrences" of those treatments in the block, namely, 0.4.

It will be helpful to consider the design in Table 6.1, which is of the same general type as the one used by Youden in his study of tobacco virus.

Table 6.1
Example of a design of type T

Block	Treatments			
I	A	B	E	F
II	A	B	D	G
III	A	C	D	F
IV	A	C	E	G
V	B	C	D	E
VI	B	C	F	G
VII	D	E	F	G

[1] This approach to the classification of nonorthogonal designs has been set out in the *Journal of the Royal Statistical Society*, Series A, 126:353–377.

First of all, each treatment occurs four times, neither more nor less, but this does not end the regularity, because the total of weighted concurrences over all blocks is 0.5 whichever pair of treatments is chosen. Thus, for A and B it is

$$\tfrac{1}{4}(1 \times 1) + \tfrac{1}{4}(1 \times 1) + \tfrac{1}{4}(1 \times 0) + \tfrac{1}{4}(1 \times 0) + \tfrac{1}{4}(0 \times 1) \\ + \tfrac{1}{4}(0 \times 1) + \tfrac{1}{4}(0 \times 0)$$

and for C and F,

$$\tfrac{1}{4}(0 \times 1) + \tfrac{1}{4}(0 \times 0) + \tfrac{1}{4}(1 \times 1) + \tfrac{1}{4}(1 \times 0) + \tfrac{1}{4}(1 \times 0) \\ + \tfrac{1}{4}(1 \times 1) + \tfrac{1}{4}(0 \times 1)$$

The same is true of all other pairs.

Further, though this is a consequence of what has already been noted, the weighted concurrences of a treatment with itself sum to the same amount for all treatments. Thus, for treatment A it comes to

$$\tfrac{1}{4}(1^2) + \tfrac{1}{4}(1^2) + \tfrac{1}{4}(1^2) + \tfrac{1}{4}(1^2) + \tfrac{1}{4}(0^2) + \tfrac{1}{4}(0^2) + \tfrac{1}{4}(0^2) = 1$$

and for treatment G it is

$$\tfrac{1}{4}(0^2) + \tfrac{1}{4}(1^2) + \tfrac{1}{4}(0^2) + \tfrac{1}{4}(1^2) + \tfrac{1}{4}(0^2) + \tfrac{1}{4}(1^2) + \tfrac{1}{4}(1^2) = 1$$

In fact, the design has a high degree of pattern even though this is not obvious at first glance. It is said to be of type T or to possess "total balance."

Where, as here, (1) a design is of type T, and (2) the block sizes are all equal, and (3) are less than the number of treatments, and where (4) no treatment ever occurs more than once in a block, the design is said to be in "balanced incomplete blocks." These constitute the first class of nonorthogonal designs to receive serious study, and they remain a most important

Table 6.2
Complement of the
design in Table 6.1

Block	Treatments		
I	C	D	G
II	C	E	F
III	B	E	G
IV	B	D	F
V	A	F	G
VI	A	D	E
VII	A	B	C

class, not only on account of their own uses, but because they can be adapted to generate other valuable designs. They have been listed by Fisher and Yates in Tables XVII to XIX.

Given a balanced incomplete block design, other designs of type T are easily generated. For example, starting with the design in Table 6.1, the "complement" is found by putting into a block those treatments that were omitted from it in the original design (Table 6.2). Also, a complete set of

Table 6.3
Extension of the design in Table 6.2

Block	Treatments									
I	A	B	C	C	D	D	E	F	G	G
II	A	B	C	C	D	E	F	F	G	G
III	A	B	B	C	D	E	E	F	G	G
IV	A	B	B	C	D	D	E	F	F	G
V	A	A	B	C	D	E	F	F	G	G
VI	A	A	B	C	D	D	E	E	F	G
VII	A	A	B	B	C	C	D	E	F	G

treatments can be added in each block to give an "extended" design, as in Table 6.3, which comes from the complement above. Finally, a design can be "doubled" as in the example in Table 6.4, though this is not usually the best way to attain efficiency.

Table 6.4
Doubling of the design in Table 6.2

Block	Treatments					
I	C	C	D	D	G	G
II	C	C	E	E	F	F
III	B	B	E	E	G	G
IV	B	B	D	D	F	F
V	A	A	F	F	G	G
VI	A	A	D	D	E	E
VII	A	A	B	B	C	C

The most valuable balanced incomplete block designs are probably the "unreduced" ones, in which use is made of all combinations of the treatments taken k at a time, k being the block size, e.g., that in Table 6.5.

Table 6.5
Example of an unreduced
design of type *T*

Block	Treatments		
I	B	C	D
II	A	C	D
III	A	B	D
IV	A	B	C

Whatever the means of generating them, designs of type T have one valuable property, namely, that all treatment comparisons are made with equal, and usually high, accuracy. In fact, it is as if all adjusted treatment means had R replicates, where R equals (the actual degree of replication) − (the sum of weighted concurrences of any treatment with itself) + (the sum of weighted concurrences of any treatment with any other treatment). Thus, in the design in Table 6.1 the effective replication was

$$(4 - 1 + \tfrac{1}{2}) = 3\tfrac{1}{2}$$

Admittedly this is less than the actual degree of replication, which was 4, but an efficiency factor of $\frac{7}{8}$ (i.e., $3\tfrac{1}{2}$ divided by 4) is good in the circumstances. Without the nonorthogonal design an experiment might not have been possible at all without ignoring one of the classifications actually taken into account.

6.2   NUMERICAL EXAMPLE OF THE ANALYSIS OF DATA FROM A DESIGN OF TYPE T

An experiment was designed to study five treatments on branches of apple trees. These were:

A, Control
B, Notching one-third from the top
C, Notching two-thirds from the top
D, Removing top third of the branch
E, Removing top two-thirds

Most of the trees available had four branches. Preliminary studies suggested that the effect of a treatment would be almost entirely confined to the branch to which it was applied, so the best design appeared to be one in which 15 trees were used as blocks. In three of the blocks treatment A was omitted, leaving B, C, D, and E; in three, treatment B was omitted; and so on. Branches were used as plots. Such a design is easily seen to be of type T because all treatments are on an equal footing.

One of the quantities to be studied was the mean length of the longest shoots from the middle third of each branch, and this was measured only for treatments A, B, and D. As a result, the data were as shown in Table 6.6. It will be seen that the resulting design is still of type T. Thus, treatments A and B have a sum of weighted concurrences of

$$\tfrac{1}{3}+0+\tfrac{1}{3}+\tfrac{1}{2}+0+\tfrac{1}{3}+\tfrac{1}{2}+\tfrac{1}{3}+0+0+0+\tfrac{1}{3}+\tfrac{1}{3}+0+\tfrac{1}{2}$$

which comes to $3\tfrac{1}{2}$; a similar value is found for A and D and for B and D. Also, the sum of weighted concurrences for A is

$$\tfrac{1}{3}+\tfrac{1}{2}+\tfrac{1}{3}+\tfrac{1}{2}+\tfrac{1}{2}+\tfrac{1}{3}+\tfrac{1}{2}+\tfrac{1}{3}+0+\tfrac{1}{2}+0+\tfrac{1}{3}+\tfrac{1}{3}+0+\tfrac{1}{2}$$

or 5, and B and D give the same value. Further, each treatment occurs 12 times, so all conditions are fulfilled.

Table 6.6
Mean length in centimeters of two longest shoots from
the middle of each branch

Block	Treatment			Total	Mean
	A	B	D		
I	87	74	80	241	80.33
II	87		75	162	81.00
III	83	77	54	214	71.33
IV	88	85		173	86.50
V	91		86	177	88.50
VI	79	78	64	221	73.67
VII	87	85		172	86.00
VIII	80	85	73	238	79.33
IX		80	64	144	72.00
X	83		90	173	86.50
XI		82	93	175	87.50
XII	92	87	66	245	81.67
XIII	82	76	87	245	81.67
XIV		76	89	165	82.50
XV	104	73		177	88.50
Total	1043	958	921	2922	

Accordingly, the effective replication for each treatment is $(12 - 5 + 3\frac{1}{2})$ or $10\frac{1}{2}$. The next task is to evaluate the values of Q, which is done in the usual way by subtracting from each treatment total the mean for each block in which the treatment occurs, thus:

$$Q_A = 1\,043 - 80.33 - 81.00 - 71.33 - 86.50 - 88.50 - 73.67$$
$$- 86.00 - 79.33 - 86.50 - 81.67 - 81.67 - 88.50$$
$$= 58.00$$
$$Q_B = 958 - 80.33 - 71.33 - 86.50 - 73.67 - 86.00 - 79.33$$
$$- 72.00 - 87.50 - 81.67 - 81.67 - 82.50 - 88.50$$
$$= -13.00$$
$$Q_D = 921 - 80.33 - 81.00 - 71.33 - 88.50 - 73.67 - 79.33$$
$$- 72.00 - 86.50 - 87.50 - 81.67 - 81.67 - 82.50$$
$$= -45.00$$

As always, the values of Q sum to zero. They provide a means of calculating the treatment sum of squared deviations; it is necessary only to square them, add the squares, and divide by the effective replication, thus:

$$\frac{(58.00)^2 + (-13.00)^2 + (-45.00)^2}{10.5}$$

This equals 529.33.

The next step is to evaluate the following summation terms:

Total   240 346.00
Blocks   109 804.00 + 128 465.00
Correction 237 169.00

It will be seen that the term for blocks has been calculated in two parts, one for blocks with three plots and one for those with two. For a one-way classification by blocks alone the analysis is therefore that in Table 6.7,

Table 6.7
Evaluation of S' for the data in Table 6.6

Source	df	Sum of squares
Blocks	14	1100.00
Error	21	2077.00 $= S'$
Total	35	3177.00

where the error is that of treatments thrown into error. Since the sum of squared deviations due to treatments is known, the full analysis is readily completed as in Table 6.8. Judged by the F test, supposing that to be appropriate, the treatments are just significantly different at the level $P = 0.05$.

Table 6.8
Full analysis of variance of the data in Table 6.6

Source	df	Sum of squares	Mean square	F
Blocks	14	1100.00		
Treatments	2	529.33	264.66	3.25*
Error	19	1547.67 = S	81.46	
Total	35	3177.00		

Adjusted treatment means are found by dividing each value of Q by the effective replication, thus obtaining 5.52, -1.24, and -4.29, and adding the general mean $(\frac{2922}{36} = 81.17)$ to each. They are therefore respectively 86.69, 79.93, and 76.88 centimeters.

The standard error of an adjusted treatment mean is always rather more than would be expected from the effective replication, i.e., it is rather larger than $\sqrt{81.46/10.5}$ or 2.79. For purposes of comparison of means, however, the effective replication gives an exact estimate. In this case the standard error of the difference of two means is $\sqrt{81.46\left(\frac{1}{10.5} + \frac{1}{10.5}\right)}$ or 3.94. With these values known, t tests can be carried out if called for. Thus, in this instance it is clear that the treatments B and D have both led to a significant $(P = 0.05)$ reduction in the length of the largest shoots.

If desired, block parameters can be obtained. Thus the total for block I is 241, made up of one plot each of A, B, and D, which account for $(86.69 + 79.93 + 76.88)$ or 243.5, leaving -2.5 to be accounted for by three block parameters, so β_1 may be estimated as -0.83. Similarly, β_2 equals $\frac{1}{2}(162 - 86.69 - 76.88)$ or -0.79. Continuing in this way, further estimates are

$$\beta_3 = -9.83 \quad \beta_4 = +3.19 \quad \beta_5 = +6.72 \quad \beta_6 = -7.50$$
$$\beta_7 = +2.69 \quad \beta_8 = -1.83 \quad \beta_9 = -6.41 \quad \beta_{10} = +4.72$$
$$\beta_{11} = +9.10 \quad \beta_{12} = +0.50 \quad \beta_{13} = +0.50 \quad \beta_{14} = +4.10$$
and $\quad \beta_{15} = +5.19$

Multiplying each parameter by the number of plots in its block and adding give 0.05, which is a reasonable approximation to zero considering the rounding-off errors.

With the block parameters known, it is easy to find the residual for any plot. Thus, for treatment A in block I it equals $[87 - 86.69 - (-0.83)]$ or $+1.14$, and so on.

A further advantage of knowing all the parameters is that they provide a check on the error sum of squared deviations, which should equal the total summation term, 240 346.00, less

$$1043(86.69) + 958(79.93) + 921(76.88) + 241(-0.83)$$
$$+ 162(-0.79) + 214(-9.83) + 173(3.19) + 177(6.72)$$
$$+ 221(-7.50) + 172(2.69) + 238(-1.83) + 144(-6.41)$$
$$+ 173(4.72) + 175(9.10) + 245(0.50) + 245(0.50) + 165(4.10)$$
$$+ 177(5.19)$$

or $(240\ 346.00 - 238\ 802.56)$ or 1543.44, which again is a reasonably good approximation.

6.3   DESIGNS OF TYPE S

The advantage of designs of type T is the complete symmetry of the treatments in respect to the design. Anything that can be asserted of one treatment can be asserted of another; anything that can be asserted of a pair of treatments can be asserted of any other pair. Of course, the means may be very different, but as far as the structure of the experiment is concerned, all treatments are on exactly the same footing. This balance is valuable for many purposes, as will appear later.

However, there are times when one of the treatments is logically on a different footing from the rest, and ideally this should be reflected in the design. For example, if it is a question of comparing each of a set of new treatments with an established one, the standard can reasonably have more plots than the others. If there is material for 30 plots, and four new treatments, A, B, C, and D, need to be compared with O, it would be better to have five blocks each with O, O, A, B, C, and D randomized on the plots, than six blocks each with O, A, B, C, and D. In the first case, O has 10 plots and each of the others 5, so for an orthogonal design the standard error of a treatment difference is

$$\sqrt{(\tfrac{1}{10} + \tfrac{1}{5})}\ \text{error mean square}$$

In the second, all treatments have 6 plots, so the standard error is

$$\sqrt{(\tfrac{1}{6} + \tfrac{1}{6})} \text{ error mean square}$$

which is more. Of course, the additional precision from doubling replication of the standard treatment has been bought at a price, because the standard error of the difference of two means of new treatments is

$$\sqrt{(\tfrac{1}{5} + \tfrac{1}{5})} \text{ error mean square}$$

which is greater than when there were six replicates. Frequently, however, the immediate task is to screen the new treatments to see if any merit further study, not to compare them among themselves. In that case, an optimal design is obtained when the degree of replication of the standard equals that of each of the new treatments multiplied by the square root of the number of new treatments. In the example, the standard has 10 plots, each of the new treatments has 5, and there are 4 new treatments; $10 = 5 \sqrt{4}$, so the ideal has been attained.

Sometimes there is no question of increasing the number of plots to receive treatment O, but rather of decreasing it. In these instances the aim is to compare the other treatments among themselves, comparison with treatment O being relatively unimportant. Thus, treatments A, B, C, etc., may be new insecticides, the aim being to select the best. However, a few plots of O (i.e., not applying insecticide) are needed; otherwise, if no insects can be found, the conclusion may be that all the insecticides were completely effective, but it could equally well be that the season was one of low infestation anyway. Quite a few plots of O may suffice to demonstrate the presence of the species, but their number needs to be kept to a minimum, for each may be a dangerous potential focus of infestation. Also, some plots of O may be needed to provide a measure of the absolute proportion killed by the various insecticides, but again the number need not be large. For these reasons, it is useful at times to relax the limitation built into designs of type T that all treatments must be equally replicated and all comparisons made with equal precision.

Nonorthogonal designs in which one treatment (the "supplementing treatment") is on a different basis from the rest, which are in total balance among themselves, are said to have "supplemented balance." It can be shown that the supplementing treatment must be in the same relationship to all the others. No one appears to have made a list of such designs, but they are very numerous, and many can be generated from balanced incomplete block designs, which have been cataloged, or from designs of type T. One method is to add a plot of treatment O to each block of a design of type T, as in Table 6.9.

Table 6.9
Design of type S obtained
by supplementation

Block	Treatments		
I	O	A	B
II	O	A	C
III	O	A	D
IV	O	B	C
V	O	B	D
VI	O	C	D

If this is done, it will be seen that O has six replicates and each of the others has three. (Since there are four of the others, this ratio is ideal if the purpose is to compare A, B, C, and D with O.) Also, O gives a sum of weighted concurrences of 1.0 with each of the others, which give a value of 0.33 among themselves. Finally, the sum of weighted concurrences of O with itself is 2.0, but it is 1.0 for any other treatment. The unique position of O and the complete equality of the other treatments is thus apparent. If designs of type T are like a community in which the sole rank is that of citizen, in those of type S there is one and only one man who stands apart, whether as king or slave, the rest insisting on complete equality among themselves in their relations both to one another and to the odd man out.

Another way of generating a design of type S is to take a design of type T and combine two or more of the treatments. Thus, if treatments F and G in the design in Table 6.1 are amalgamated to form treatment O, the result is as shown in Table 6.10. At first sight this is not of type S because

Table 6.10
Design of type S obtained by
amalgamation from that in
Table 6.1

Block	Treatments			
I	A	B	E	O
II	A	B	D	O
III	A	C	D	O
IV	A	C	E	O
V	B	C	D	E
VI	B	C	O	O
VII	D	E	O	O

treatment A appears to be in a special position, e.g., it never appears in a block with O doubled. However, it is like the others in respect to all the characteristics used in classifying designs. Thus, it has four replicates like the other nonsupplementing treatments; it has 1.0 as the sum of weighted self-concurrences, 0.5 as the sum of weighted concurrences with other non-supplementing treatments, and 1.0 as the sum with the supplementing treatments.

When designs of this type are needed with fewer plots of O than of the others, it is not difficult to form them. One possibility is to use one of the above methods and to add a further design that involves only the nonsupplementing treatments, one which is either orthogonal or of type T, e.g., as in Table 6.11 (1). In the design in Table 6.11 (2), blocks I to VI form a design of type S, and blocks VII to X are of type T.

Table 6.11
Designs of type S with fewer replicates of the supplementing treatment
(1)

Block	Treatments
I	O B C
II	O A C
III	O A B
IV	A B C
V	A B C
VI	A B C

(2)

Block	Treatments	Block	Treatments
I	O A B	VI	O C D
II	O A C	VII	B C D
III	O A D	VIII	A C D
IV	O B C	IX	A B D
V	O B D	X	A B C

All the above examples have used blocks of equal size, but many designs of type S exist in which this property is not found.

6.4[2]   NUMERICAL EXAMPLES OF THE ANALYSIS OF DATA FROM A DESIGN OF TYPE S

The analysis of data for a design in supplemented balance follows closely that for one with total balance, so in the following example only points of difference will be noted. The trial to be considered was intended to study if it was worthwhile sowing a cover crop under apple trees instead of letting natural sward develop (treatment O). Treatments A, B, C, and D were various grass mixtures, though in the actual experiment mixture D failed to germinate, and the treatment was changed to clean cultivation, i.e., no vegetable cover. On account of the need to use plots large enough for mowers and cultivators to turn, the designer was rather restricted and had to confine himself to 16 plots. However, the object was to compare O with A, B, C, and D rather than A, B, C, and D among themselves, so he used the design in Table 6.12.

Table 6.12
Design used in the apple
cover-crop experiment

Block	Treatments			
I	A	B	C	O
II	B	C	D	O
III	A	C	D	O
IV	A	B	D	O

Some years after the start of the experiment a record was made of the incidence of apple scab (*Venturia inaequalis*) on each plot, the results being those set out in Table 6.13.

The first task is to work out totals for blocks and treatments and the means for blocks, thus:

Blocks (totals)	7.9,	26.0,	15.8,	24.9	
(means)	1.975,	6.500,	3.950,	6.225	
Treatments	12.2,	11.1,	6.9,	26.5,	17.9

Both sets of totals add to a grand total of 74.6.

[2] The reading of this section can be postponed until its contents are needed.

Table 6.13
Venturia data from the apple cover-crop
experiment

Block	Treatment				
	A	B	C	D	O
I	2.5	1.5	1.4		2.5
II		4.7	4.3	10.4	6.6
III	3.3		1.2	7.3	4.0
IV	6.4	4.9		8.8	4.8

Values of Q are now readily determined, thus:

$$Q_A = 12.2 - 1.975 - 3.950 - 6.225 = +0.050$$
$$Q_B = 11.1 - 1.975 - 6.500 - 6.225 = -3.600$$
$$Q_C = 6.9 - 1.975 - 6.500 - 3.950 = -5.525$$
$$Q_D = 26.5 - 6.500 - 3.950 - 6.225 = +9.825$$
$$Q_O = 17.9 - 1.975 - 6.500 - 3.950 - 6.225 = -0.750$$

A check on these values is provided by their summing to zero.

The effective replication of the nonsupplementing treatments is found as for a design of type T. It is therefore $(3 - \frac{3}{4} + \frac{1}{2}) = 2.75$. The effective replication for the supplementing treatment is derived from it. First the sum of weighted concurrences of treatment O with one of the others is worked out; here it is 0.75, and this value is multiplied by 2.75 to give 2.0625. Then the sum of weighted concurrences between two nonsupplementing treatments is found (0.5) and divided into 2.0625 to give 4.125, the effective replication of treatment O. It may seem odd that this value exceeds the actual replication (4), but it should be recalled that these effective replications relate solely to comparisons. That for treatments A to D is low. For comparison of these with treatment O, any deficiency of effective replication on the one side must be balanced by an increase on the other. Since treatment O is meant to be well compared with the rest, it is not really surprising that its effective replication is so high.

From the above results, the treatment sum of squares is readily found. It equals

$$\frac{Q_A{}^2 + Q_B{}^2 + Q_C{}^2 + Q_D{}^2}{2.75} + \frac{Q_O{}^2}{4.125}$$

or 51.0523.

The summation terms are:

T (total)	456.0800
T_1 (blocks)	402.0150
T_0 (correction)	347.8225

These enable the total sum of squared deviations to be calculated and partitioned into components between and within blocks. Knowledge of the treatment sum of squared deviations enables the latter to be partitioned further. This is done in Table 6.14, and completes the computation of the analysis of variance.

Table 6.14
Analysis of variance for the apple cover-crop experiment

Source	df	Sum of squares	Mean square
Blocks	3	54.1945	
Treatments	4	51.0523	
Error	8	3.0127	0.3766
Total	15	108.2575	

The adjusted treatment means are found easily enough. The first step is to divide each value of Q by the corresponding effective replication, thus:

$$\frac{Q_A}{2.75} = +0.0182$$

$$\frac{Q_B}{2.75} = -1.3091$$

$$\frac{Q_C}{2.75} = -2.0091$$

$$\frac{Q_D}{2.75} = +3.5727$$

$$\frac{Q_O}{4.125} = -0.1818$$

There is a constant, Z, which needs to be added to each of these to give the means required. Expressions exist for its estimation, but the simplest procedure is to use the fact that the grand total of 74.6 is made up of three plots each of A, B, C, and D, and four of O. Therefore

$$74.6 = 3(Z + 0.0182) + 3(Z - 1.3091) + 3(Z - 2.0091)$$
$$+ 3(Z + 3.5727) + 4(Z - 0.1818) = 16Z + 0.0909$$

so Z equals 4.6568, and the adjusted treatment means are

A, $4.6568 + 0.0182 = 4.675$
B, $4.6568 - 1.3091 = 3.348$
C, $4.6568 - 2.0091 = 2.648$
D, $4.6568 + 3.5727 = 8.230$
O, $4.6568 - 0.1818 = 4.475$

Standard errors of difference between adjusted treatment means are readily found; formulas are the same as for orthogonal designs except that effective replicates are used instead of actual. Thus, for the difference between treatments A and B the standard error is $\sqrt{\left(\dfrac{1}{2.75} + \dfrac{1}{2.75}\right)}\,0.3766$, and for the difference of A and O it is $\sqrt{\left(\dfrac{1}{2.75} + \dfrac{1}{4.125}\right)}\,0.3766$, or 0.523 and 0.478 respectively. From the latter figure it appears that the least significant difference $(P = 0.05)$ between the natural sward standard and any of the other treatments is 2.306×0.478, or 1.10, because 2.306 is the value of t for 8 degrees of freedom and $P = 0.05$. It follows then that, at the significance level stated, the sowing of mixtures B and C has reduced the incidence of *Venturia* compared with the infection arising with natural sward; on the other hand, clean cultivation, D, has increased it.

The check on the error line and the estimation of residuals can proceed by the method given in Chapter 5, the one difference arising from the fact that the general parameter α and the treatment parameter γ have not been obtained separately but as adjusted treatment means, that is, $\alpha + \gamma$. However, this is something of a simplification.

Thus, the total for block I is 7.9, which should equal $4\alpha + 4\beta_1 + \gamma_A + \gamma_B + \gamma_C + \gamma_O$. This may be written

$$(\alpha + \gamma_A) + (\alpha + \gamma_B) + (\alpha + \gamma_C) + (\alpha + \gamma_O) + 4\beta_1$$
$$= 4.675 + 3.348 + 2.648 + 4.475 + 4\beta_1$$

so β_1 can be estimated as -1.812. Similarly, β_2, β_3, and β_4 should be estimated as $+1.825$, -1.057, and $+1.043$ respectively. It will be seen that these values satisfy the equation of constraint for block parameters, i.e.,

$$4\beta_1 + 4\beta_2 + 4\beta_3 + 4\beta_4 = -0.004$$

which is in good agreement.

It is now possible to obtain a further evaluation of the error sum of squared deviations. It should be

$$T - 7.9\beta_1 - 26.0\beta_2 - 15.8\beta_3 - 24.9\beta_4 - 12.2(\alpha + \gamma_A)$$
$$- 11.1(\alpha + \gamma_B) - 6.9(\alpha + \gamma_C) - 26.5(\alpha + \gamma_D) - 17.9(\alpha + \gamma_O)$$
$$= 456.0800 - 7.9(-1.812) - 26.0(1.825)$$
$$- 15.8(-1.057) - 24.9(1.043) - 12.2(4.675)$$
$$- 11.1(3.348) - 6.9(2.648) - 26.5(8.230) - 17.9(4.475)$$
$$= 3.0082$$

which again is reasonably close. Also, residuals are easily found. For example, that for the first plot (treatment A in block I) is

$$2.5 - \alpha - \beta_1 - \gamma_A$$
$$= 2.5 - (\alpha + \gamma_A) - \beta_1$$
$$= 2.5 - 4.675 - (-1.812)$$
$$= -0.363 \text{ or about } -0.4$$

Other residuals can be found with equal ease.

6.5   DESIGNS OF TYPE G

Designs with group balance, i.e., those of type G, belong to a wider class, described as being "partially balanced" and form quite the most important part of it. They arise only when the treatments fall into groups of equal size. Their characteristics are (1) that all treatments of a group are totally balanced among themselves and (2) that groups as a whole are totally balanced.

Suppose, for example, that an experimenter starts with a simple design of type T like this:

Block	Treatments	
I	Y	Z
II	X	Z
III	X	Y

Now he makes X, Y, and Z into groups instead of single treatments, e.g., X represents treatments A and B, Y represents C and D, and Z represents E and F. The design is now:

Block	Treatments			
I	C	D	E	F
II	A	B	E	F
III	A	B	C	D

which is of type G.

There are many other designs of this type, e.g., that in Table 6.15. Here there is great emphasis on comparisons within the groups ABC and DEF and much less on comparisons like A with E or C with D.

Table 6.15

Example of a design of type G

Block	Treatments			
I	A	D	E	F
II	B	D	E	F
III	C	D	E	F
IV	A	B	C	D
V	A	B	C	E
VI	A	B	C	F

It will help to work out the characteristics of the treatments. Each has four replicates; each gives a sum of weighted concurrences of 1.0 with itself, of 0.75 with members of its own group, and of 0.50 with members of another group. For a design to be of type G, all these values must be the same whichever treatment is taken.

The principal use of these designs comes with factorial sets of treatments, and these will be discussed later when the uses of such designs have become apparent. It will suffice here to comment that occasions arise when treatments form natural groups and that it is more important to make accurate comparisons within a group of similar treatments than between members of two dissimilar groups. For this reason alone, designs of type G deserve attention.

6.6[3]   NUMERICAL EXAMPLE OF THE ANALYSIS
OF DATA FROM A DESIGN OF TYPE G

The following data were taken from an investigation in which a second set of treatments was applied to a completed experiment. The design therefore had three classifications: blocks, former treatments, and current treatments.

The material consisted of 48 Napoleon cherry trees. In the former experiment there were eight blocks, I to VIII, and six spraying treatments, 1 to 6. Subsequently six fresh treatments, A to F, were applied. A was an unsprayed control; B to F were copper fungicides which, it was feared, might injure the trees if used to control fungal pests upon them. It was therefore decided to try them upon the trees of this completed experiment; the data to be used represent cherry crops in the following year. As to the former treatments, these could well have left residual effects that would lead to differential cropping, but it was hard to believe that these effects would make a tree more or less susceptible to copper damage. Accordingly, they formed in effect a second blocking system of differences to be eliminated.

The new treatments were allocated in the way shown by Table 6.16.

Table 6.16
Design adopted in the
fungicide experiment

Block	Former treatments					
	1	2	3	4	5	6
I	E^1	C	F	D	B	A
II	A	E	B	F	C	D
III	E	F	B	D	C	A
IV	D	B	A	C	F	E
V	B	F	D	A	E	C
VI	F	A	C	E	D	B
VII	D	E	A	F	B	C
VIII	C	D	E	B	A	F

[1] A–F are current treatments.

Taking in turn the three pairs of classifications, (1) the former treatments were orthogonal to blocks, (2) the current treatments had been ap-

[3] The reading of this section can be postponed until its contents are needed.

plied so that they also were orthogonal to blocks, and (3) it was not possible to dispose the current treatments orthogonally to the former ones. The design is in fact of type G, the groups being ABC and DEF. It will be noticed that in each column there are two treatments that occur twice, and they are always in the same group.

Following the method for three-way classifications, blocks will first be ignored, leaving a diminished design with two classifications, i.e., former treatments or "blocks" and current treatments or "treatments." The data are set out in Table 6.17.

Table 6.17
Data (crops in pounds) from a cherry-spraying trial with group balance (Diminished design)

"Treatment"	"Block"					
	1	2	3	4	5	6
A	16.7	7.2	12.3 10.9	11.7	15.0	9.2 10.4
B	18.6	8.1	10.1 5.4	15.3	7.3 16.7	13.3
C	13.1	7.6	16.3	13.5	7.5 8.9	15.7 19.3
D	8.9 12.7	13.8	17.9	14.6 15.5	9.8	9.6
E	12.8 13.6	9.9 9.4	15.3	12.2	10.0	17.4
F	12.5	1.2 15.9	7.8	9.0 10.9	10.9	10.3

The first task is to work out "block" totals, "block" means, and "treatment" totals, which are as follows:

"Block" totals: (1) 108.9   (2) 73.1   (3) 96.0   (4) 102.7
(5) 86.1   (6) 105.2

"Block" means: (1) 13.6125   (2) 9.1375   (3) 12.0000
(4) 12.8375   (5) 10.7625   (6) 13.1500

"Treatment" totals: (A) 93.4 (B) 94.8 (C) 101.9 (D) 102.8 (E) 100.6
(F) 78.5

The grand total is 572.0

Following the usual method it appears that

$$Q_A = -3.2500 \quad Q_B = +0.5375 \quad Q_C = +6.4875$$
$$Q_D = +4.8500 \quad Q_E = +6.3500 \quad Q_F = -14.9750$$

For a design of this type it is also useful to have the total values of Q within groups. Here,

First total, $(Q_A + Q_B + Q_C) = +3.7750$

Second total, $(Q_D + Q_E + Q_F) = -3.7750$

The effective replication of a treatment with regard to others of its own group is found exactly as for a design of type T. Here it equals

$$(8 - 1.5 + 1.375) = 7.875$$

The sum of squared deviations for treatments within groups can now be obtained as a difference of two summation terms. The first is

$$\frac{Q_A{}^2 + Q_B{}^2 + Q_C{}^2 + Q_D{}^2 + Q_E{}^2 + Q_F{}^2}{7.875} = 43.3060$$

The second is that for the totals of the groups, i.e.,

$$\frac{(3.7750)^2}{3 \times 7.875} + \frac{(-3.7750)^2}{3 \times 7.875} = 1.2064$$

so the sum of squared deviations of treatments within groups is 42.0996, i.e., $(43.3060 - 1.2064)$.

Next the effective replication between groups needs to be found. The method is (1) to find the sum of weighted concurrences for two treatments in the same group (1.375 in this instance) and for two in different groups (1.250) and to take the difference (0.125); (2) to multiply by the number of treatments in a group; and (3) to subtract the result (0.375) from the effective replication within groups (7.875). This gives 7.5 for an individual treatment, or 22.5 for the group as a whole.

Continuing the evaluation of the treatment sum of squared deviations, the component between groups also equals the difference of two summation terms. The first is

$$\frac{(3.7750)^2}{22.5} + \frac{(-3.7750)^2}{22.5} = 1.2667$$

The second equals zero because the values of Q necessarily sum to zero and thus give a nil summation term. The sum of squared deviations for treatments is therefore

$$42.0996 + 1.2667 = 43.3663$$

taking into account variation both between and within groups.

Since error and "treatments" together make up the variation within "blocks," the analysis for the diminished design can be completed. Three summation terms are needed, namely,

T (total)   7,483.0400
T_1 ("blocks")   6,930.7950
T_0 (correction)   6,816.3333

The analysis is given in Table 6.18.

Table 6.18
Analysis of variance for the diminished design of the fungicide experiment

Source	df	Sum of squares
"Blocks"	5	114.4617
"Treatments"	5	43.3663
Error	37	508.8787
Total	47	666.7067

The sole remaining task is to work out the sum of squared deviations for the ignored classification. This requires the block totals (true blocks, not former treatments), which are:

I, 59.3;   II, 62.8;   III, 55.0;   IV, 71.1;
V, 89.8;   VI, 71.3;   VII, 79.9;   VIII, 82.8

and give a summation term of 6,988.0200. The full analysis is therefore that in Table 6.19.

Table 6.19
Analysis of variance for the full design of the fungicide experiment

Source	df	Sum of squares	Mean squares
Blocks	7	171.6867	
Former treatments	5	114.4617	
Current treatments	5	43.3663	8.6733
Error	30	337.1920	11.2397
Total	47	666.7067	

It does not appear that the current treatments can have had much effect.

If a check on the error is needed, it is most conveniently made on that of the diminished design.

A check will require the adjusted treatment means, which are the same in the full and the diminished designs. To obtain them it is necessary to note that the general mean is $572.0/48 = 11.9167$. This first needs to be adjusted by group means, using the effective replication appropriate to comparison between groups, e.g., the adjusted mean for the first group is

$$11.9167 + \frac{3.7750}{22.5} = 12.0845$$

and for the second,

$$11.9167 + \frac{-3.7750}{22.5} = 11.7489$$

Adjustments within groups should be made using the other value for effective replication. Thus the mean for treatment A is

$$\frac{Q_A}{7.875} - \frac{3.7750}{3 \times 7.875}$$

above its group mean. This adjustment equals

$$-0.4127 - 0.1598 \text{ or } -0.5725$$

The adjusted mean for A is therefore $[12.0845 + (-0.5725)]$ or 11.512. For the other treatments it is B, 11.993; C, 12.749; D, 12.525; E, 12.715; and F, 10.008. Residuals may be found by the method of Chapter 5.

The analysis for the three-way classification having been completed, there is no difficulty in carrying out the usual tests and estimates. As was explained in the last chapter, if the treatments had been orthogonal to both the other classifications, everything would have been as for an orthogonal design. Since, however, they were not orthogonal to former treatments, efficiencies are as for the diminished design. Let R be the effective replication within groups, i.e., 7.875, and let R' be that between groups, i.e., 22.5, and let R^0 equal

$$\frac{nRR'}{nR + (n-1)R'}$$

where n is the number of treatments in a group. Here $n = 3$, so $R^0 = 7.746$. Then the standard error of a difference of treatment means, both treatments being in the same group, is

$$\sqrt{2 \text{ error mean square}/R}$$

If they are in different groups, it is

$$\sqrt{2 \text{ error mean square}/R^0}$$

As an approximation, the standard error of an adjusted treatment mean is written

$$\sqrt{\text{Error mean square}/R^0}$$

CHAPTER SEVEN

MISSING DATA

AN EXPERIMENT HAS BEEN CAREFULLY
DESIGNED AND THEN SOMETHING GOES
WRONG WITH THE PLANS; IT IS SHOWN THAT
MUCH OF THE DESIRED INFORMATION CAN
OFTEN BE SALVAGED FROM THE WRECK.

In any experiment the loss of data is vexatious. Where there has been careful planning to provide figures for a certain form of analysis, an accident can appear little short of disastrous, though happily so extremely pessimistic a view is rarely justified. It is usually possible to salvage much of the information needed, but it must be said clearly that a defective experiment loses on two counts. First, there are fewer data on which to base estimates and tests; secondly, the arbitrary distortion of an experimental design necessarily leads to less efficient use of the data that remain. Consequently, there is always loss of information, the proportionate loss usually exceeding the proportion of lost data.

7.1   THE ESTIMATION OF MISSING PLOT VALUES

There are several ways of dealing with a gap in the data of an orthogonal design. One is to accept the data as they stand and to treat them as if the design were nonorthogonal, but this is indeed a "desperate remedy." A better way is to estimate what the missing datum would have been. It is this approach that leads to misunderstanding because, the gap having been filled, everything looks as if nothing had happened; this impression is sadly wrong.

In order to estimate the missing value it is only necessary to fill the gap with a value that makes its residual equal to nothing; there is then no contribution to error. Thus, in the pea growth-substance experiment, suppose that the value for gibberellic acid in block II had been unobtainable because someone had dropped a tool and damaged all the plants in that plot. Let the missing datum be replaced by a value m, still to be evaluated. The data are now as in Table 7.1.

The residual, which must be made equal to zero, equals

$$m - \frac{317 + m}{6} - \frac{198 + m}{4} + \frac{1444 + m}{24}$$

Table 7.1
Data of pea growth-substance experiment with a plot missing

	Block				
	I	II	III	IV	
Untreated control	60	62	61	60	243
Gibberellic acid	65	m	68	65	198 + m
Kinetin	63	61	61	60	245
Indole acetic acid	64	67	63	61	255
Adenine sulphate	62	65	62	64	253
Maleic hydrazide	61	62	62	65	250
	375	317 + m	377	375	1444 + m

Hence, multiplying by 24 and separating knowns from unknowns,

$$15\,m = (4 \times 317) + (6 \times 198) - 1444 = 1012$$

so $m = 67.467$, which will be approximated to 67. (As was mentioned in Chapter 4, the expression for evaluating a residual is derived from the formula for working out the error sum of squared deviations from the summation terms.)

All that remains is to work out the analysis of variance as if the data were complete. However there are now only 23 data, so there will only be 22 degrees of freedom in all. Also, one of the plots will be making no contribution to error, which will therefore have only 14 degrees of freedom instead of 15. The modified analysis is now that in Table 7.2. It is not very

Table 7.2
Analysis of variance for the data in Table 7.1

Source	df	Sum of squares	Mean square
Blocks	3	9.13	
Treatments	5	78.21	
Error	14	39.62	2.8300
Total	22	126.96	

different in its general implications from the one with complete data. Nevertheless, there is the loss of 1 degree of freedom from error. Also, the mean for gibberellic acid is determined with less accuracy than before. For both randomized blocks and Latin squares from which a single plot has been lost, the standard error of the defective treatment mean is

$$\sqrt{\frac{t+f}{rf}} \text{ error mean square}$$

instead of

$$\sqrt{\frac{\text{Error mean square}}{r}}$$

where r is the number of plots the treatment was intended to have, f is the number of error degrees of freedom intended, and t is the number of treatments. So in this instance the standard error of the mean for gibberellic acid has been raised from

$$\sqrt{\frac{\text{Error mean square}}{4}} \qquad \text{to} \qquad \sqrt{\frac{7 \text{ error mean square}}{20}}$$

Similarly, the standard error of a difference of treatment means, one of them defective, is raised from

$$\sqrt{\frac{2 \text{ error mean square}}{r}} \qquad \text{to} \qquad \sqrt{\frac{t + 2f}{fr} \text{ error mean square}}$$

or in this instance from

$$\sqrt{\frac{\text{Error mean square}}{2}} \qquad \text{to} \qquad \sqrt{\frac{3 \text{ error mean square}}{5}}$$

If several plots are missing, all their residuals can be made equal to zero, a degree of freedom being removed from both the total and error lines for each datum missing. This is done in the same way as before, but simultaneous equations must be solved to find the missing plot values. Thus, in the pea growth-substance experiment it could have been that a second plot was missing, as in Table 7.3.

$$0 = m_1 - \frac{255 + m_1 + m_2}{6} - \frac{198 + m_1}{4} + \frac{1\,382 + m_1 + m_2}{24}$$

$$0 = m_2 - \frac{255 + m_1 + m_2}{6} - \frac{188 + m_2}{4} + \frac{1\,382 + m_1 + m_2}{24}$$

Multiplying both equations by 24 and separating knowns and unknowns give

$$15m_1 - 3m_2 = 826$$
$$-3m_1 + 15m_2 = 766$$

Hence $m_1 = 68$, and $m_2 = 65$. Using these values, 2 degrees of freedom need to be removed from both total and error lines.

Table 7.3
Data for pea growth-substance experiment with two plots missing

	Block				
	I	II	III	IV	
Untreated control	60	62	61	60	243
Gibberellic acid	65	m_1	68	65	$198 + m_1$
Kinetin	63	61	61	60	245
Indole acetic acid	64	67	63	61	255
Adenine sulphate	62	65	62	64	253
Maleic hydrazide	61	m_2	62	65	$188 + m_2$
	375	255 $+m_1 + m_2$	377	375	1382 $+m_1 + m_2$

Again defective treatment means are less well determined than the others. Precise formulas will not be given, but the standard error of a defective treatment mean is never better than what it would be in an orthogonal design with the same number of actual plots. If nonorthogonality is severe, the accuracy may be much less than this.

7.2   EFFECTS OF NONORTHOGONALITY IN A DEFECTIVE ORTHOGONAL DESIGN

Using the technique presented above, the nonorthogonality of the data has been ignored. Actually, if more than 80 per cent of the data have been preserved, there is little need to bother about it, but the full procedure for dealing with disasters needs to be known. It will be illustrated using the example already given (Table 7.1) of a plot missing from the pea growth-substance experiment, though admittedly in this instance the nonorthogonality was not very serious.

In analyzing any body of data, the logical basis, as has been said, lies in the determination of two errors, the one including the effects of treatments and the other excluding them. If the former is significantly larger, the treatments are judged to have had an effect.

Thus, in the pea experiment with one missing plot, if treatments are counted as part of the error, there is only a one-way classification, and the formula for the error sum of squared deviations is

$$S' = T - T_1$$

so
$$0 = m - \frac{317 + m}{6}$$

therefore $\quad m = 63$

Adopting this value, $T - T_1$ equals 107.17 with 19 degrees of freedom. Keeping treatments separate, the smaller error, S, has already been found to be 39.62 with 14 degrees of freedom. The difference, 67.55 with 5 degrees of freedom, is correctly attributed to treatments. This is rather less than 78.21, the figure obtained ignoring the nonorthogonality. If a number of plots had been missing, the nonorthogonality might well have been more serious. Whatever the number of missing plots, the method is always the same. There are three steps: (1) Missing plot values are fitted for the design as it stands and S is worked out; (2) The treatments are thrown into error, thus making a design with one classification fewer, a fresh set of missing plot values is obtained, and a fresh error, S', evaluated; (3) The difference between the two errors, $S' - S$, is attributed to treatments. The error found in (1) is the true one.

When adjustment is made for nonorthogonality, the treatment sum of squared deviations is reduced, the error line being unaffected. Consequently the only effect can be to reduce the significance of the differences between treatments.

7.3   OTHER METHODS OF DEALING WITH DEFECTIVE DATA

The method given is a very usual one, though it has certain disadvantages. One is that, in the form given, it can be used only for designs that are initially orthogonal; another is the need to solve several simultaneous equations when several plots are missing.

Two other methods merit study. One, which involves the analysis of covariance, will be given later; the other is a matter of simple, if extensive, arithmetic. Both methods apply regardless of design, and the second, which will now be presented, is ideal for use with electronic computers.

The missing values are first filled in by guesswork. The same final answer will be found whatever values are used, but the better the initial guesses, the sooner the job will be done. Suppose, for example, in the case where one plot has been lost from the growth-substance trial, that the experimenter fills the missing value with the guess 63. This makes the block total 261, the treatment total 380, and the grand total 1,507. The block mean is therefore 65.25, the treatment mean 63.33, the general mean 62.79, and the residual (63.00 − 65.25 − 63.33 + 62.79) or −2.79. The residual is then multiplied by the number of plots in the experiment as planned, i.e.,

$$(-2.79)24 = -66.96$$

and the product divided by the number of error degrees of freedom as planned, i.e.,

$$\frac{-66.86}{15} = -4.46$$

which quantity is subtracted from the guessed value, i.e.,

$$63.00 - (-4.46) = 67.46$$

to give a better approximation than the guess. It will be seen that the new approximation is in fact the missing plot value except for a small rounding-off error.

This will always be so if (1) only one plot is missing and (2) the design belongs to a rather restricted class, which, however, contains some very common designs, e.g., randomized blocks, Latin squares, and balanced incomplete blocks.

The method can be used just as well when several plots are missing. Thus, in the growth-substance experiment when two values are missing, these could be guessed as 67 and 64. The residuals are then respectively

$$67.00 - 66.25 - 64.33 + 63.04 = -0.54$$
and $\quad 64.00 - 63.00 - 64.33 + 63.04 = -0.29$

Multiplied by the number of plots, these become −12.96 and −6.96. Dividing by the number of error degrees of freedom gives −0.86 and −0.46, which suggest 67.86 and 64.46 as better approximations than the ones obtained by guesswork.

This time there is more than one plot missing, so the values just found cannot be accepted without further examination, but this is done easily enough by repeating the process until the residuals are reduced to zero, a process known as "iteration." Using the new values, the residuals are respectively

$$67.86 - 66.47 - 64.55 + 63.10 = -0.06,$$
and $$64.46 - 63.12 - 64.55 + 63.10 = -0.11$$

For data expressed to the nearest integer these residuals may well seem negligible. However, if needed, they produce fresh approximations, namely, $[67.86 - 24(-0.06)/15]$ or 67.96, and $[64.46 - 24(-0.11)/15]$ or 64.64. These are indeed good ones, the residuals now being

$$67.96 - 66.49 - 64.60 + 63.11 = -0.02$$
and $$64.64 - 63.16 - 64.60 + 63.11 = -0.01$$

With nonorthogonal designs this method is possible, though the method of calculating residuals can render it laborious. With several missing plots, however, an experimenter without an electronic computer may well be daunted by the thought of a long sequence of approximations, each better than the last but none of them good. This fear will be accentuated if he has come to mistrust his ability to guess well in the first place. However, whatever method is used, with many plots missing from a complicated design there will be difficulty. This is a reason, when deaths of experimental plants and animals are expected to occur, for using only orthogonal designs. Whatever method of fitting missing plot values is adopted, the values when found are used as if they were data, and the analysis proceeds normally apart from the adjustment of the degrees of freedom.

Of course it is always permissible to use the general method of Chapter 5. The labor here is in evaluating the treatment parameters. With only two treatments the general method may be quite simple; with three it can still be manageable; but with more it is rarely worthwhile. Incidentally, this approach will not give the same result as the others. The analysis of variance will be the same and so will differences between the adjusted treatment means, but the means themselves will all have drifted up or down by a constant amount. The reason for this lies in the different value of the general parameter in the two methods. When missing plot values are fitted, the total experimental area remains unchanged and the general parameter represents an average performance of all treatments over it; when the missing plots are ignored, the general parameter represents an average over the plots that remain. It is this that causes the drift of values.

7.4   STATISTICAL TESTS FOR THE REJECTION OF PLOTS

If there is doubt about a plot value being aberrant or not, it is always possible to test the significance of its residual. In fact, the calculations have already been effectively carried out for the value rejected in Table 7.1. First the error sum of squared deviations, S, is found for the case where the residual is eliminated, i.e., for the case where the plot is rejected. It equals 39.62, with 14 degrees of freedom (Table 7.2). Then S' is found, namely, the sum of squared deviations when the residual is allowed to assume its apparent value. This equals 43.30, with 15 degrees of freedom (Table 3.4), so the analysis of variance is that of Table 7.4. Plainly, from an F test, there is nothing odd about this particular residual.

Table 7.4

Source	df	Sum of squares	Mean square
Suspect residual	1	3.68	3.68
Error	14	39.62	2.83
Total	15	43.30	

It may be noted that when a single datum is first included and then excluded, if the design belongs to the restricted class mentioned above, $S' - S$ equals

$$\frac{fd^2}{N}$$

where f is the number of degrees of freedom for the full design ($f = 15$), N the number of plots in the full design ($N = 24$), and d the deviation of the observed datum from the missing plot value. Here d equals 2.467, so $S' - S$ would be expected to equal 3.80, and therefore S should equal 39.50. The discrepancy may be explained thus: In Tables 7.2 and 7.4 the missing plot has been taken as 67, when strictly speaking it should have been 67.467. Accordingly, in Table 7.4 the fitted value is still in error by 0.467, so the error sum of squares found exceeds its true value by

$$\frac{15(0.467)^2}{24} = 0.14$$

which is nearly correct. In fact, once Table 7.2 had been found, Table 7.4 could have been calculated better using the formula just given.

Where doubt attaches to several plots, the same approach can be used; S is calculated with all plots excluded, S' with them all included. S is taken as error and $S' - S$ as due to the residuals considered collectively. A difficulty arises when there are two sets of doubtful plots, e.g., there have been two accidents. The best procedure here is to take each set separately. First S' is worked out including all plots of both sets, and then S, excluding only those plots doubtful for one of the reasons, and a decision is reached concerning these. Afterwards S is worked out again, excluding only those doubtful for the second reason, and a decision is reached. The analysis is then completed excluding none, one, or both of the sets, whichever may have been indicated.

This is a useful technique, but one open to abuse. For one thing, a residual should not be tested just because it is large. If twenty residuals chosen at random are tested at the level $P = 0.05$, it is to be expected that one of them will be judged significant. The situation is not altered by testing only the largest, i.e., the one most likely to show up. Also, if a residual has been tested and found not to be suspiciously large, it would be wrong to leave the plot in the experiment. Plainly, if the sum of squares for the residual is kept separate when it is large and added to error when it is small, the effect will be to bias the estimate of error. Its separation will have provided information for another time whether such a mishap is or is not serious; for the experiment currently under study it is enough to say that there were genuine doubts about the plot and it was therefore excluded.

It may be objected that this amounts to saying that an experimenter who does not like a certain value has only to declare that it is suspicious and it will thereafter be excluded whether there is really anything wrong with it or not. Of course, this is not the intention. No value should ever be excluded because it is distasteful. The whole purpose of an experiment is to call in experience to decide a doubtful point, and the experience must not be tampered with if it is to be cited in evidence. A value can never be "suspicious" just because it goes against accepted ideas; the grounds for rejection must always be some objective fact, e.g., the animal has become diseased, the plant has been damaged, or a measuring instrument has been broken.

7.5   REJECTION IN DIFFICULT SITUATIONS

In any difficulty, two questions should be asked. First, does the doubt arise from an objective fact or does the experimenter dislike the value because it seems to him aberrant? Secondly, is its residual remarkably large or not? According to the answers, four situations can be discerned.

1. Objective fact, residual large. In this case the value is rejected without reservation.

2. Objective fact, residual not large. The value should be rejected this time, but the experimenter should remember not to be so particular in the future.

3. Subjective dislike, residual large. It would often be best to quote a conclusion with the value retained, but add that the result has been largely brought about by one aberrant figure. If the plot is to be rejected, it must be on some grounds other than the experimenter's dislike of it, and the one reason for taking the matter further would be the large residual. This could well lead to a detailed examination of the plot to see if it had been damaged in any way. (Of course, a determined man can find something wrong with anything, so the examination will provoke fewer sardonic comments if it is carried out by a disinterested colleague.) If something unusual is found, the other plots should be examined too, so that any others damaged in the same way can be rejected also. Finally, the question may arise whether the plot should not be rejected simply because it has a large residual, but here caution is needed. As has been pointed out, if there are 20 plots and the residual of each is tested for significance at the level $P = 0.05$, it is to be expected that one of them will prove to be significantly large. If only the largest is tested, very probably it will prove to be significant, but so would it also if the data had been abstracted from a table of random numbers. This is a case where a protective significance level is useful. If there are N plots and each residual is tested for significance at the level P, then the probability of one or more of the residuals being found significant is p, where

$$N \log (1 - P) = \log (1 - p)$$

Suppose then that there are 20 plots ($N = 20$) and that it is desired to test each residual at some significance level P, so that overall there will be only one chance in twenty ($p = 0.05$) of rejecting the largest residual even though it is really all right. Then $\log (1 - p) = \log 0.95 = \bar{1}.97772 = -0.02228$. Hence $\log (1 - P) = -0.001114 = \bar{1}.998886 = \log 0.9974$, so P should be taken as 0.0026. (Much the same result would have been obtained using the approximation $NP = p$.) The difficulty is to find tables for the unusual protective significance levels required; often it is possible to do no more than make a good guess.

4. Subjective dislike, residual not large. Plainly there are no grounds for rejecting the value.

7.6   BIOLOGICAL CONSIDERATIONS

At first sight a plot is clearly missing or it is not, but often it is not easy to decide. Thus in an experiment on the incidence of parasites the plot might be a standard length of intestine, each plot from a different animal. Clearly a distinction would be needed between plots that were missing and those in which no parasites were found, 0 being just as much a number as 8 or 88. On the other hand, the fact that a plot is missing sometimes indicates the value to be ascribed to it. Suppose, for example, that an experiment is in progress to compare different methods of propagating a plant species. In one plot all the plants die, giving a zero value for survival. The investigator now turns his attention to growth. Does he regard the plot as missing for purposes of this variate, or is it one that has made zero growth? If he believes that the plants died because the treatments killed them, he would prefer to record the plot as having not grown. If, on the other hand, deaths were fairly general over the experiment, and he believes that this plot just happened to be unlucky, he would prefer to put a missing plot value. Either course could be reasonable, but he should act on some clear principle to avoid a charge of caprice.

Indeed, many difficulties arise from having to decide whether or not the loss of the plot is a consequence of the treatment applied. With few exceptions an experimenter should abide by his data; if a treatment is associated with a lot of missing plots, he must assume that it has lethal effects unless he can see clearly that the plots are missing for some other reason. But such a decision will not end his troubles. For one thing, he may ascribe zero values to plots that die, but an array of data with many zeros rarely gives a homogeneous error and is rarely additive. For another, if plots die, it may not be possible to record them. Thus, in the propagation experiment a dead plant may be said to have made no growth, but for the date of the first leaf there is no effective alternative to a missing plot value. In decisions of this sort the statistician usually has little part to play beyond warning the experimenter of the need to discard nothing without an objective reason. Especially should nothing be discarded just because it leads to awkward conclusions. This is brazen cheating, amounting to analyzing only such data as conform to the experimenter's expectations.

An interesting example of the decisions that often have to be made is the experiment referred to in Chapter 2 about the effect of previous diet on the incidence of toxaemia during pregnancy. Much of the nutritional data was obtained by questioning the expectant mothers. One set of answers appeared to be absurd, and it was then realized that the patient concerned was a foreigner with a very poor grasp of the language, so it was thought better to exclude her from the investigation. It is true that tests could have been carried out to discover if residuals relating to her were peculiar. However, she still could not have been included in the current experiment, and the information gained would have applied only to her and not to foreigners in general. Also, it would have proved very little if residuals relating to her had been shown to be unusual, because in respect to diet she probably was different from the other women, though this might have made her especially useful if it had been possible to include her.

The next decision to be made concerned a woman who, it appeared as the experiment progressed, was going to have triplets. However, advice on diet sometimes has to be given before it is known whether the pregnancy will result in a multiple birth or not, and it was decided to include her so that the experiment should refer to the population ostensibly under study. Finally, some patients were regarded as missing plots because they had a history of essential hypertension, a factor that a medical practitioner could take into account and which might affect the incidence of toxaemia.

This example neatly illustrates most of the considerations that enter into a decision to exclude a plot. These are rarely statistical, but derive rather from background biological knowledge and respect for the purpose of the experiment.

CHAPTER EIGHT

PARTITIONS OF THE SUM OF SQUARED DEVIATIONS FOR TREATMENTS

IF THE TREATMENTS ARE RELATED

TO ONE ANOTHER IN A LOGICAL SCHEME,

THE ANALYSIS OF VARIANCE CAN OFTEN BE

TAKEN A STAGE FURTHER SO AS TO ANSWER

MORE SPECIFIC QUESTIONS.

In previous chapters various experimental designs have been described, and for all of them it has been possible to partition the total sum of squared deviations into components, one of which relates to treatments. In this chapter further partitioning of the treatment component will be considered.

8.1   INDIVIDUAL DEGREES OF FREEDOM

The comment was made earlier that in an F test all the degrees of freedom for treatments are tested together. If all comparisons are of the same kind, this may be a reasonable procedure, but usually the set of treatments has been chosen with a good deal of thought so as to contain within itself a number of specific comparisons, each of which has its individual interest. The experimenter will not want these to be put together into one heap and subjected to a comprehensive test in which the small differences can dilute the large ones and make the whole nonsignificant. Further, one comparison may depend upon the opinion formed of another, e.g., an investigator might use two drugs that he believed would have similar effects and a third that he wished to compare with them. He would have 2 degrees of freedom, one of which related to the difference between the first two drugs. Only if the sum of squared deviations associated with it proved to be nonsignificant would he take the second degree of freedom and ask if there was indeed a difference between the third drug and the first two; if the two supposedly similar drugs proved to be different, the second question would have little meaning.

Care should be observed in any instance where the carrying out of one test depends on the result of another. If he is not wary, an experimenter finds himself saying, "Because A and B were not significantly different, they must have given the same result. I therefore regarded them as the same treatment, which I compared with C." This would be wrong because lack of significance in a difference does not prove identity. He should say, "I had reason to believe that A and B would give similar results, but I was ready to think I might be mistaken. However, the data did not suggest that I was, so I went ahead and compared them with C." In fact, the whole argument implies a reasonable presupposition about the similarity of A and B. Alternatively, it implies that A and B had something in common. Thus, they might both be applications of a fertilizer, but at different times, whereas C was the absence of such fertilization. It would then be reasonable to ask first if it mattered when the fertilizer was applied and then, if it made much difference whether the fertilizer was applied or not.

It cannot be said too firmly that skill in interpreting data depends principally on recognizing the function of each of the degrees of freedom associated with the treatments. A good experimenter knows why each treatment was included, i.e., which comparisons it was intended to facilitate. He can then test these comparisons and no others, and is able to carry out his tests in their logical order. Against him are bad experimenters of two kinds, those who never distinguish individual degrees of freedom at all, but use only comprehensive tests, and those who distinguish them on some basis other than the logic of the experimental situation, e.g., who test only the largest differences irrespective of what they mean. The former finds too little and the latter too much; each uses statistical methods to his own destruction.

8.2   PARTITIONING WITH AN ORTHOGONAL DESIGN WITH ALL TREATMENTS EQUALLY REPLICATED

In most orthogonal designs all the treatments occur on the same number of plots, say n. Where this is so, partitioning of the treatment sum of squared deviations is easy.

Suppose, to take an example, that (1) there are four treatments and (2) the experimental situation requires that the mean of treatment A be compared with the means of treatments B, C, and D regarded collectively. Writing A for the total of treatment A, B for that of treatment B, and so on, this comes to asking if

$$\frac{A}{n} - \frac{B + C + D}{3n}$$

equals zero. This contrast will be written

$$\left\{ \frac{1}{n}, \ -\frac{1}{3n}, \ -\frac{1}{3n}, \ -\frac{1}{3n} \right\}$$

the four values representing the coefficients of the four treatment totals. However, it would not affect the situation if all the coefficients were multiplied by some constant; the difference would still equal zero or not as before. Accordingly, as a matter of convenience and for no other reason, all will be multiplied by $3n$ to give the contrast $\{3, \ -1, \ -1, \ -1\}$. The one limitation on writing contrasts is that the coefficients should sum to zero; otherwise it is not to be expected that the difference will do so.

The sum of squares for the contrast just given is

$$\frac{(3A - B - C - D)^2}{12n}$$

The numerator has been found by multiplying each treatment total by the corresponding coefficient and squaring the sum; the 12 in the denominator equals the sum of the coefficients squared, i.e., $3^2 + (-1)^2 + (-1)^2 + (-1)^2$. The sum of squares has 1 degree of freedom.

It might also be tempting to take a degree of freedom for the difference of treatment B from the rest, but this would not be ideal because successive degrees of freedom should preferably relate to information independent of what is already known. If this condition is not observed, the sum of squares will not add up correctly. Independence is readily investigated by multiplying out coefficients and adding. Thus, here the comparisons are

$$\{ \ 3, \ -1, \ -1, \ -1\}, \text{ i.e., } A \text{ versus the rest}$$
and $\quad \{-1, \quad 3, \ -1, \ -1\}, \text{ i.e., } B \text{ versus the rest}$

However, $3(-1) + (-1)3 + (-1)(-1) + (-1)(-1)$ equals -4. If the comparisons had been independent, the sum of products would have been zero, as with

$$\{3, \ -1, \ -1, \ -1\}$$
and $\quad \{0, \quad 2, \ -1, \ -1\}$

The second of these comparisons is that of treatment B with the mean of C and D, and represents the further breaking down of a group of treatments left intact in the first comparison. This gives a clue as to the information left.

The third degree of freedom between the four means is in fact the comparison of C and D, the only treatments that have yet to be differentiated, i.e.,

$$\{0, \quad 0, \quad 1, \quad -1\}$$

which is independent of each of the first two.

It should be emphasized that there are many other ways in which the comparisons between four treatments can be broken down into 3 independent degrees of freedom. Thus, there are 12 methods like the above, depending on the order in which the treatments are separated out. There is also

$$\{1, \quad 1, \quad -1, \quad -1\}$$
$$\{1, \quad -1, \quad 1, \quad -1\}$$
$$\{1, \quad -1, \quad -1, \quad 1\}$$

and three like

$$\{1, \quad 1, \quad -1, \quad -1\}$$
$$\{1, \quad -1, \quad 0, \quad 0\}$$
$$\{0, \quad 0, \quad 1, \quad -1\}$$

There is no point in asking which is correct. Any could arise from the nature of a problem being studied. What is certainly wrong is to partition and repartition until something significant is found. By examining enough degrees of freedom and giving each a twentieth chance of appearing significant, an adroit manipulator can find something in a table of random numbers. The position is analogous to the use of the t test; a partition should be avoided unless it is indicated by study of the experimental situation.

8.3   PARTITIONING IN OTHER CIRCUMSTANCES

The method given needs modification where the degree of replication, either actual or effective, varies from treatment to treatment.

This situation can occur in orthogonal designs where each block contains, say, two plots of A and one each of B, C, D, and E. Such a situation is easily dealt with, because for purposes of partition it is as if there had initially been six treatments, A_1, A_2, B, C, D, and E, and the difference between the first two had been studied by isolating the degree of freedom for

$$\{1, \quad -1, \quad 0, \quad 0, \quad 0, \quad 0\}$$

Further partitions may take place provided they are independent of this one.

Indeed, some people would carry out the analysis of variance for such a design by first arbitrarily allotting plots of A to mythical treatments A_1 and A_2 so as to form a design in which each treatment occurred once in each block. They would then calculate its analysis of variance, work out the sum of squared deviations for

$$\{1, \quad -1, \quad 0, \quad 0, \quad 0, \quad 0\}$$

and transfer it with 1 degree of freedom from the treatment line to the error. The method seems cumbersome, but it neatly exemplifies the approach.

It may be asked how one is to decide which plot belongs to A_1 and which to A_2. The answer is that it does not matter. Once the difference between A_1 and A_2 is eliminated, only their combined totals are ever required.

The situation is not essentially different if there were, say, two plots of A, one of B, and three of C in each block. It is then as if there had been six original treatments, A_1, A_2, B, C_1, C_2, and C_3, and 1 degree of freedom for the difference of A_1 and A_2 had been eliminated as well as 2 for the differences between C_1, C_2, and C_3, that is, as if

$$\{1, \quad -1, \quad 0, \quad 0, \quad 0, \quad 0\}$$
$$\{0, \quad 0, \quad 0, \quad 2, \quad -1, \quad -1\}$$
and $\quad\{0, \quad 0, \quad 0, \quad 0, \quad 1, \quad -1\}$

had all been removed. Thereafter, further degrees of freedom may be separated out provided they are independent of those shown.

With nonorthogonal designs similar situations sometimes arise. Those of type T are easy because all comparisons are made equally well. The values of Q are used instead of treatment totals, and the effective replication, R, instead of the actual replication, n. Partitioning then takes place as with an orthogonal design.

With designs of type S the position is much the same. Let R_0 be the degree of effective replication of the supplementing treatment, and let R be the corresponding figure for the others. The treatment sum of squared deviations equals

$$\frac{Q_0{}^2}{R_0} + \frac{Q_A{}^2}{R} + \frac{Q_B{}^2}{R} +, \text{etc.}$$

That part which corresponds to the difference between the supplementing treatment and all the rest is

$$Q_0{}^2 \left(\frac{1}{R_0} + \frac{1}{vR} \right)$$

where v is the number of nonsupplementing treatments. The remainder is

$$\frac{(Q_A{}^2 + Q_B{}^2 +, \text{etc.})}{R} - \frac{(Q_A + Q_B +, \text{etc.})^2}{vR}$$

because $(-Q_0)$ equals the sum of the other values of Q. It will be seen that what remains has the form of the treatment sum of squares for a design of type T, and further partitions may take place freely. In fact, the one constraint is the need to begin by taking out the comparison of the supplementing treatment and the rest. Thereafter there are none.

For designs of type G the error has already been given as a sum of two components, one for variation between groups and one for variation within. Either of these may be partitioned freely within itself. It is important that the appropriate value for the degree of effective replication be used in each case.

8.4   LINEAR, PARABOLIC, AND CUBIC EFFECTS

One specially important case arises when the treatments are differentiated quantitatively and are equally spaced, e.g., the application of 0, 200, or 400 pounds of fertilizer per acre. Sometimes the spacing is proportionate, as when 100, 1,000, or 10,000 predators are introduced into a standard population; occasionally more complicated situations arise. The essential condition for present purposes is that the middle treatment can reasonably be regarded as lying halfway between the other two. The question is whether the response of the middle treatment lies halfway between the responses of the others, i.e., if the two outside treatments give means of 200 and 300, does the middle one give 250? It would be an extraordinary coincidence if it gave exactly that value, but a test might well be required to find out if the deviation from the expected value was significant. Actually, the question is whether the effect of the middle treatment differs from the mean effect of the outside ones, i.e., it concerns the contrast $\{1, \quad -2, \quad 1\}$. This is called the "parabolic" effect, because it measures the extent to which the response curve must be regarded as a parabola instead of a straight line.

The other degree of freedom corresponds to the contrast $\{1, \quad 0, \quad -1\}$, which relates to the difference between the outside treatments. If there is no parabolic effect, i.e., if the response curve is a straight line, this contrast shows if there is any differential effect of treatments at all. It is called the "linear" effect. On account of the relationship between the three treatments it has been possible to partition the 2 degrees of freedom and, further, to establish the logical order of the two tests. Of course, if it is clear that the response relationship is curved, it would be wrong to proceed to the second test. A better next step would be to establish the shape of the curve.

With four equally spaced treatments, the partitions are as follows:

$$\{3, \quad -1, \quad -1, \quad -3\}$$
$$\{1, \quad -1, \quad -1, \quad 1\}$$
and $\quad \{3, \quad 1, \quad -1, \quad -3\}$

The first of these picks up any inflection of the curve, i.e., any tendency for it to adopt a sigmoid form—concave first on one side and then on the other. If there is no evidence of this, the second effect compares the two inside treatments with the two outside ones, i.e., it provides a test of curvature. If the response to the treatments, supposing one to exist, is straight (a point to be established by the two tests just given), then the third effect provides a test whether or not there is a response.

Tests of this kind can be most valuable, and their existence points a need for a sequence of quantitative treatments to be evenly spaced, like 0, 1, 2, 3, or 1, 2, 4, 8. Some people incline to series like 0, 1, 2, 4, which can be very awkward; the first three terms are in arithmetic progression and the last three in geometric, with no recognizable progression over the complete set. The idea usually is to find an optimum application or dose and to express its response in terms of the effect of no treatment at all. Where this is clearly understood, the best procedure is to partition out the difference between the null treatment and the rest, and then to consider the response curve between the rest. The optimum having been found, it is expressed as "percentage kill" or "relative growth" or whatever may be appropriate. Incidentally, when a treatment is introduced only to provide a basis of measurement for the others, there is no need for it to have as many replicates as they have. Consequently, designs of type S are often useful.

8.5   A NUMERICAL EXAMPLE

A good example is afforded by the experiment on times of cutting hay. Here the treatments formed two groups, A, B, and C on the one hand and D and E on the other, so the natural first degree of freedom is $\{2, \quad 2, \quad 2, \quad -3, \quad -3\}$. Within the first group the treatments form an equally spaced set of one or two or three earlier cuttings, and this suggests the degrees of freedom

$$\{-1, \quad 0, \quad 1, \quad 0, \quad 0\}$$
$$\{\ 1, \quad -2, \quad 1, \quad 0, \quad 0\}$$

The first studies the general effect of changing the number of cuttings, the second whether the response is curved or not. The remaining degree of freedom represents the difference between the two treatments in the other group, i.e.,

$$\{0, \quad 0, \quad 0, \quad -1, \quad 1\}$$

It will be seen that any pair of these contrasts is independent, so their sums of squares should add up correctly. In fact, the partitioning of the treatment sum of squares goes as in Table 8.1.

Table 8.1
Partition of treatment sum of squares in the grass-cutting experiment

Source	df	Sum of squares	F
Between groups	1	2 057 330	13.33**
Group I, linear	1	2 190	<1
parabolic	1	90 970	<1
Within Group II	1	7 904 988	51.22***
Between treatments	4	10 055 478	

Apart from the rounding-off error, the sum of squares add up correctly. The error mean square is known to be 154 333, so it is possible to work out F for each contrast and to judge its significance. Also, 51.22 is close to 7.17^2, showing the F test to be equivalent to the t test used previously. However, the calculation performed here is simpler than the earlier one and has a simple check. It also shows the contrast of E with A, B, and C to be in a special position, because

$$\{1, \quad 1, \quad 1, \quad 0, \quad -3\}$$

is not independent of the others. Accordingly, although the contrast corresponds to a natural question, the answer is to some extent implicit in what has already been found. Also, the contrast

$$\{2, \quad 2, \quad 2, \quad -3, \quad -3\}$$

although it represents independent information, has no real meaning because it compares the means of two groups, one of which contains diverse treatments, D and E, and therefore is not a fit subject for generalization.

8.6   A FACTORIAL PARTITION

It often happens that the treatments of an experiment are arrived at by taking all possible combinations of two other sets of treatments. For example, four drugs are to be compared and each is administered either four times a day in half-doses or twice a day in full ones; or three teaching methods are to be studied and each is tried on children of industrial, suburban, and rural backgrounds. A set of treatments so derived is said to be "factorial" and usually requires a characteristic partitioning of the treatment sum of squares.

Each of the above examples would be described as having two factors: in the first instance one is at four levels and the other at two; in the other, both factors are at three levels. More fully, the first would be said to have 4×2 treatment combinations and the second to have 3^2. This method of stating the number of treatments makes clear the factorial structure.

A simple example is afforded by an experiment on the gain in live weight of lambs. There were four grazing treatments, derived factorially from the use of two grass mixtures, A and B, either strip grazed (S) or rotationally grazed (R). There were four pure Clun lambs to a plot, and the variate was the gain in weight from April 1 to July 21 of the same year. Data are set out in Table 8.2.

Table 8.2
Data from a grazing experiment (increase in weight of four lambs in pounds)

Treatment	Block				
	I	II	III	IV	
AS	254	269	251	248	1022
AR	276	270	262	265	1073
BS	205	204	250	232	891
BR	231	242	254	249	976
	966	985	1017	994	3962

These data lead to the summation terms $T = 987\,734.00$, $T_1 = 981\,426.50$, $T_2 = 985\,567.50$, and $T_0 = 981\,090.25$, and hence to the analysis in Table 8.3.

Table 8.3
Analysis of variance for the data in Table 8.2
(Treatment line not partitioned)

Source	df	Sum of squares	Mean square
Blocks	3	336.25	
Treatments	3	4477.25	
Error	9	1830.25	203.36
Total	15	6643.75	

From an F test it is clear that treatments are having an effect, but the question arises which factor is the operative one.

Calling the factors M, for mixture, and G, for grazing, the treatment summation term, T_2, may better be written T_{MG}, to indicate that it relates to classification of the data by both factors, M and G. Further, the totals may be written so as to display their factorial structure. They can then be added both horizontally and vertically, as in Table 8.4.

Table 8.4
Factor totals from the data in Table 8.2

	A	B	
S	1022	891	1913
R	1073	976	2049
	2095	1867	3962

Two further summation terms may now be obtained, namely,

$$T_M = \tfrac{1}{8}(2095^2 + 1867^2) = 984\,339.25$$
and $\quad T_G = \tfrac{1}{8}(1913^2 + 2049^2) = 982\,246.25$

Hence, two components of the treatment sum of squared deviations are readily derived:

$$T_M - T_0 = 3249.00$$
$$T_G - T_0 = 1156.00$$

each with 1 degree of freedom and representing respectively the difference between mixtures averaged over grazings and that between grazings averaged over mixtures. However there is a sum of squares left of $T_{MG} - T_M - T_G + T_0 = 72.25$ with one further degree of freedom and it is not at once apparent what it represents.

However, this method of partitioning is not basically different from the one already given. The two contrasts extracted have been that of AS, AR, against BS, BR, and that of AS, BS, against AR, BR, namely,

$$
\begin{array}{cccc}
AS & AR & BS & BR \\
\{\,1, & 1, & -1, & -1\,\} \\
\{\,1, & -1, & 1, & -1\,\}
\end{array}
$$

The degree of freedom left must refer to a contrast independent of both of these, since it is defined to make the several components add up to the sum of squared deviations for treatments. The contrast is, in fact

$$\{1, \quad -1, \quad -1, \quad 1\}$$

This amounts to a test of

$$AS - AR - BS + BR$$

being zero. However, if it is,

$$(BR - AS) = (BS - AS) + (AR - AS)$$

The left-hand side of this equation represents the result of simultaneously changing A to B and S to R. The two terms on the right-hand side represent the results of making the changes in isolation. Only if the factors operate independently will the two sides of the equation come to the same thing. The factors are then said not to "interact" and the contrast $\{1, \quad -1, \quad -1, \quad 1\}$ accordingly provides a test of this possible "interaction," which will be written $M \times G$. The full analysis is that in Table 8.5.

Table 8.5
Analysis of variance for the data in Table 8.2 (Treatment
line partitioned)

Source	df	Sum of squares	Mean square	F
Blocks	3	336.25		
M	1	3249.00	3249.00	15.98**
G	1	1156.00	1156.00	5.68*
M × G	1	72.25	72.25	<1
Error	9	1830.25	203.36	
Total	15	6643.75		

It is always a sound practice to interpret analyses of variance from the bottom upward. First, the error line shows if an accurate experiment has been carried out. Then, the interaction line shows if the factors can be considered to operate independently. It appears that they can, so the results can be expressed by saying that strip grazing was significantly less effective ($P < 0.05$) for fattening lambs than rotational grazing, and that mixture A was significantly better ($P < 0.01$) than B. If, however, there had been an interaction, it would have been necessary to present a two-way table, because it would not have been meaningful to average grazings over mixtures or mixtures over grazings.

8.7   MORE GENERAL FACTORIAL PARTITIONS

The method to be given now applies generally, whatever the number of levels for each factor. First, the ordinary summation term is worked out for the treatment combinations. If the factors are X and Y, it will be written T_{XY}, and it will have $(xy - 1)$ degrees of freedom, where x and y are the number of levels for X and Y respectively. Next, totals are taken for each factor in turn, and these are used to compute further summation terms, T_X and T_Y. The sum of squared deviations for the main effect of X is then $(T_X - T_0)$ with $(x - 1)$ degrees of freedom; for the main effect of Y it is $(T_Y - T_0)$ with $(y - 1)$ degrees of freedom; and for their interaction it is $(T_{XY} - T_X - T_Y + T_0)$ with $(x - 1)(y - 1)$ degrees of freedom.

The similarity to partitioning the total sum of squares of a randomized block experiment will be noticed. This is no coincidence. If treatments had exactly the same effect in all blocks, i.e., if there were no interaction of blocks and treatments, there would be no error.

The method may readily be extended for three or more factors. Suppose, for example, that there are four, W, X, Y, and Z. First the treatment combination totals are written down in tabular form. Then tables are derived from this basic one, excluding the four classifications in turn, i.e., leaving X, Y, and Z; W, Y, and Z; W, X, and Z; and W, X, and Y. There is no immediate way of checking these derived tables, but one will appear later. The next step is to obtain tables classifying by two factors at a time, and each of these may be obtained in two ways. Thus, that for X and Y can be derived from that for W, X, and Y and also from that for X, Y, and Z, thus providing the desired check on the earlier tables. Finally, totals for the four factors separately can be obtained in three ways, those for W, for example, being obtainable from the tables for W and X, W and Y, and W

and Z. Finally, the grand total, which is already known, can be obtained in four ways, thus checking the whole computation.

Summation terms are now obtained for each table and the partition of $(T_{WXYZ} - T_0)$ with $(wxyz - 1)$ degrees of freedom is carried out as in Table 8.6. This time higher-order interactions appear, such as $W \times X \times Y$; these correspond to effects that arise only when certain combinations of levels of several factors occur together. For example, a disease may be transmitted when certain strains of the pathogen are used, a certain inoculation technique is employed, and the host is in a certain condition; otherwise it is not transmitted.

Table 8.6
Partitioning of a four-factor experiment

Source	df	Sum of squares
W	$(w - 1)$	$T_W - T_0$
X	$(x - 1)$	$T_X - T_0$
Y	$(y - 1)$	$T_Y - T_0$
Z	$(z - 1)$	$T_Z - T_0$
W × X	$(w - 1)(x - 1)$	$T_{WX} - T_W - T_X + T_0$
W × Y	$(w - 1)(y - 1)$	$T_{WY} - T_W - T_Y + T_0$
W × Z	$(w - 1)(z - 1)$	$T_{WZ} - T_W - T_Z + T_0$
X × Y	$(x - 1)(y - 1)$	$T_{XY} - T_X - T_Y + T_0$
X × Z	$(x - 1)(z - 1)$	$T_{XZ} - T_X - T_Z + T_0$
Y × Z	$(y - 1)(z - 1)$	$T_{YZ} - T_Y - T_Z + T_0$
X × Y × Z	$(x - 1)(y - 1)(z - 1)$	$T_{XYZ} - T_{YZ} - T_{XZ} - T_{XY} + T_X + T_Y + T_Z - T_0$
W × Y × Z	$(w - 1)(y - 1)(z - 1)$	$T_{WYZ} - T_{YZ} - T_{WZ} - T_{WY} + T_W + T_Y + T_Z - T_0$
W × X × Z	$(w - 1)(x - 1)(z - 1)$	$T_{WXZ} - T_{XZ} - T_{WZ} - T_{WX} + T_W + T_X + T_Z - T_0$
W × X × Y	$(w - 1)(x - 1)(y - 1)$	$T_{WXY} - T_{XY} - T_{WX} - T_{WY} + T_W + T_X + T_Y - T_0$
W × X × Y × Z	$(w - 1)(x - 1)(y - 1)(z - 1)$	$T_{WXYZ} - T_{XYZ} - T_{WYZ} - T_{WXZ} - T_{WXY}$ $+ T_{WX} + T_{WY} + T_{WZ} + T_{XY} + T_{WZ} + T_{YZ}$ $- T_W - T_X - T_Y - T_Z + T_0$

The general rule for an interaction sum of squares is to write down the summation term for all the factors involved, subtract all terms that omit one of the factors, add all that omit two, and so on, till the correction term is reached. Degrees of freedom equal the product of those for the main effects of the factors involved.

An F test is then worked out for each line, starting from the most complex interaction. However, if an interaction is found to be significant, there is no point in testing any other effect contained in it. Thus, if $W \times Y \times Z$ is significant, it means that there are results that arise only for certain combinations of these three factors, and the correct procedure is to present a three-way table to make this apparent, not to test lines like $W \times Z$ or $Y \times Z$ or W.

8.8   SPLIT PLOTS

When there are several factors, they do not all have to be applied to plots of the same size. Thus, a herd of cows must all be fed the same way, but methods of milking can be different for each animal. Consequently, in an experiment involving both factors it might be advisable first to design a trial for the study of feeding regimes using groups of animals as plots and then to split these plots into "subplots" of a single cow each, there being one cow per plot for each milking method. Again, it might be suspected that a certain necrotic condition arises whenever plants infected with a virus receive mechanical damage. Only whole plants can be infected with virus, so these must form the plots, but single laminae can be damaged, and these might well form subplots for application of the other factor.

Split-plot designs are of many kinds, but they are usually adopted for one of two reasons. Sometimes it is scarcely practicable to apply both factors to plots of the same size. The design is then adopted for reasons of practical convenience. Sometimes, on the other hand, it provides a means of placing emphasis, because the interaction and the factor on the subplots are ordinarily studied more precisely than the factor on the main plots. For example, a trial might be designed in order to find which strawberry varieties were adversely affected by a range of weed killers. For practical reasons it would be easier if all plots of one variety, which will be picked about the same time, were close together. On the other hand, weed killer can be applied to quite small areas; it would therefore be convenient to use a split-plot design. Also, it places the emphasis where it is needed, because the experimenter is not trying to compare the varieties; indeed, he has probably chosen them on the basis of well-known characteristics. He does, however, want to know about the weed killers and their interaction with varieties. With the weed killers on the subplots, these treatments gain in precision what the varieties on the main plots lose. Sometimes, of course, the two considerations conflict; it would perhaps be more convenient to have factor A on main plots, but this would place the emphasis on B, which is possibly of value only as providing an interaction. In such an instance careful judgment is needed. A compromise might be to avoid split plots altogether, applying both factors to plots of the same size. Certainly this keeps the design simple.

The process can be carried further, the subplots being split into sub^2-plots for a third factor, and so on. However, there is no need for each factor to have its own level of splitting. Thus, factors A and B could be applied to main plots, C to subplots, D and E to sub²plots, and F, G, and H to sub³plots. Such an experiment would be very complicated, but quite valid.

8.9   THE ANALYSIS OF DATA FROM EXPERIMENTS WITH SPLIT PLOTS

An analysis is needed for each level of splitting. To take an example, the time-of-cutting experiment already described really had split plots, because each of the main plots was divided into four subplots, one for each of four grass mixtures, W to Z. The full data were as shown in Table 8.7.

Table 8.7
Full data (i.e., including grass mixtures) for the grass-cutting experiment

CW 648	BW 453	EW 1032	DW 562	AW 452
X 532	X 463	X 933	X 540	X 427
Y 323	Y 294	Y 1215	Y 407	Y 439
Z 434	Z 309	Z 827	Z 511	Z 449
DW 392	EW 781	AW 739	CW 630	BW 624
X 528	X 759	X 826	X 568	X 490
Y 493	Y 588	Y 632	Y 567	Y 618
Z 299	Z 890	Z 550	Z 523	Z 508
AW 489	CW 499	DW 529	BW 456	EW 1204
X 620	X 551	X 673	X 366	X 958
Y 400	Y 428	Y 422	Y 554	Y 967
Z 476	Z 294	Z 676	Z 510	Z 950
BW 610	AW 378	CW 759	EW 826	DW 432
X 976	X 436	X 734	X 1104	X 677
Y 509	Y 354	Y 457	Y 866	Y 383
Z 457	Z 336	Z 602	Z 1380	Z 449
EW 1036	DW 289	BW 626	AW 911	CW 596
X 765	X 511	X 445	X 918	X 1020
Y 474	Y 339	Y 601	Y 704	Y 438
Z 704	Z 256	Z 466	Z 551	Z 632

If these quantities are added in fours, the totals will be those already given in Table 3.9 for the Latin square. In fact, the whole of the analysis of variance for the main plots is implicit in what has already been done, the only difference being that the data, which previously represented single observations, now equal the sum of four. Hence, the summation terms already obtained need to be divided by four.

Proceeding to the analysis for subplots, the design is clearly analogous to one in randomized blocks, the main plots serving as blocks. Hence the total sum of squares of the first analysis is the block sum of squares of the second. It will also be necessary to work out totals for the subplot treatments; these are given in Table 8.8.

Table 8.8
Totals for treatment combinations for the data in Table 8.7

Cutting treatment	Grass mixture				
	W	X	Y	Z	
A	2969	3227	2529	2362	11 087
B	2769	2740	2576	2250	10 335
C	3132	3405	2213	2485	11 235
D	2204	2929	2044	2191	9 368
E	4879	4519	4110	4751	18 259
	15 953	16 820	13 472	14 039	60 284

The following summation terms are required:

T_i (main plots)	40 083 094.50
T_{ii} (subplots)	41 554 576.00
T_1 (rows)	37 048 625.50
T_2 (columns)	36 399 207.90
T_{CM} (cuttings and mixtures)	39 331 566.40
T_C (cuttings)	38 855 476.20
T_M (mixtures)	36 639 956.56
T_0 (correction)	36 341 606.56

T_i, T_1, T_2, T_M, and T_0 were obtained in Chapter 3, but here they are divided by four.

It is now possible to write down the full analysis of variance. The first part, that for main plots, is as for a Latin square; the second part includes the subplot factor (M) and the interaction $(C \times M)$. Its error sum of squares equals the additional sum of squares brought about by introducing the subplots $(T_{ii} - T_i)$, less the values due to the main effect $(T_M - T_0)$

and the interaction $(T_{CM} - T_C - T_M + T_0)$, that is, it equals $(T_{ii} - T_i - T_{CM} + T_C)$, a quantity that will be studied in more detail later. The analysis is therefore as in Table 8.9.

Table 8.9
Analysis of variance for the data in Table 8.7

Source	df	Sum of squares	Mean square
Rows	4	707 018.94	
Columns	4	57 601.34	
Cutting (C)	4	2 513 869.64	628 467.41
Error i	12	462 998.02	38 583.17
Total i = Blocks ii	24	3 741 487.94	
Mixtures (M)	3	298 350.00	99 450.00
C × M	12	177 740.20	14 811.68
Error ii	60	995 391.30	16 589.86
Total ii	99	5 212 969.44	

The F value for the interaction is less than one, so there is no reason to suspect that the cutting treatments have had different effects on the four grass mixtures. Each factor can therefore be studied without reference to the other.

The effects of cutting were examined at some length in Chapter 3, and the same results would have been obtained from the first part of the analysis just presented. It is true that the error mean square has only a quarter of its previous value. Also, each mean is based on four times as many data, so the quantity under the square-root sign in the expression for standard errors, etc., has only one-sixteenth of its former value. Hence, the standard error is reduced to one-quarter of what it was before. The means also have one-quarter their former value, because they are now based on subplots instead of main plots, so relatively, everything is as it was before.

The grass mixtures are evidently different,

$$F = 99\ 450.00/16\ 589.86 = 5.99**$$

though this could hardly have been in doubt. The important conclusion is the absence of an interaction, i.e., recommendations about cutting do not have to be qualified by stating the grass mixture, at least not within the range studied here.

As usual, the second analysis is more sensitive than the first, the error mean square being 16,589.86 instead of 38,583.17.

The method of calculating the error mean square of the second analysis will repay some examination. The treatments applied to subplots may form a number of grass-mixture experiments, each under a different cutting regime. Each has five blocks (the number of main plots for each cutting treatment) and four mixtures, so each has 12 degrees of freedom. Since there are five such experiments, there should be 60 degrees of freedom for Error ii, which is in fact so. Also, each will have an error sum of squares made up of four summation terms:

(1) for the subplots
(2) for the blocks, i.e., main plots
(3) for the mixtures within the cutting treatment
(4) for the total of the cutting treatment

Adding these terms over all five cutting treatments gives $T_{ii} - T_i - T_{CM} + T_C$, the expression used previously.

This alternative way of looking at the second analysis is useful when subplots are missing. Thus, if the first datum, 648 for CW in row 1 and column 1, were lost, it could be fitted from the other values under treatment C without reference to those from the other four cutting treatments. It is as if a plot were missing from a randomized block experiment like the one in Table 8.10.

Table 8.10
Data from one component of that in Table 8.7

Treatment	Block				
	I	II	III	IV	V
W	m	499	759	630	596
X	532	551	734	568	1020
Y	323	428	457	567	438
Z	434	294	602	523	632

Hence m is fitted as 483, thereby reducing to 59 the degrees of freedom for Error ii. Also, the sum of squares for Error ii would be reduced by $\frac{12}{20}(648 - 483)^2$, because each of the five components of Error ii exists independently of the others.

8.10   SOME MORE COMPLICATED CASES

Sometimes it is not possible to randomize a factor on the subplots. For example, if an experiment is being conducted with animals as plots, and each is observed on a number of occasions, there is, in effect, a split-plot design, but the occasions, which form the subplot factor, obviously cannot be randomized. Or again, an experiment may use plant shoots as plots, each shoot having a number of leaves. A botanist might well inquire whether young leaves and old leaves react to the main-plot treatments in the same way, but if he regards leaf position as a subplot factor, he will encounter the objection that it cannot be randomized.

This difficulty can, however, be overcome. The remedy is to work out the interaction of the systematic factor and blocks and to subtract it from Error ii; what remains is unvitiated by the lack of randomness. It can therefore be used for the study of the interaction. No valid analysis can be carried out for the main effect of the systematic factor.

There is no reason for using only one split; as has been said, the process can be continued. As each size of plot is reached, a further analysis is required, the total line of the preceding analysis being the block line of the new. Each analysis contains (1) the main effects of factors applied to that size of plot, (2) their interactions one with another, and (3) their interactions with factors previously considered. The error sum of squares is obtained by an extension of the method previously given. Thus, if, as suggested previously, factors A and B were applied to main plots, C to subplots, and D and E to sub^{2}plots, the sum of squares for Error iii would equal $T_{iii} - T_{ii} - T_{ABCDE} + T_{ABC}$, where T_{iii} is based on sub^{2}plot values and T_{ii} on subplot values. Its degrees of freedom would be those for abc experiments, each of r blocks of de treatments, that is, $abc(r-1)(de-1)$, where a, b, c, d, and e are respectively the number of levels of factors A, B, C, D, and E, and r is the number of replicates in the experiment on main plots. The abc components, each with $(r-1)(de-1)$ degrees of freedom, could be considered separately if missing plots needed to be fitted.

CHAPTER NINE

INTERACTIONS AND CONFOUNDING

THE PARTITIONING DESCRIBED IN CHAPTER 8 HAS AN ESPECIALLY USEFUL FORM IN SOME INSTANCES. ALSO, SOMETIMES IT IS POSSIBLE TO SACRIFICE INFORMATION OF LITTLE INTEREST TO LEARN MORE ABOUT MATTERS OF GREATER IMPORTANCE.

"I KNEW WHEN SEVEN JUSTICES COULD NOT TAKE UP A
QUARREL, BUT WHEN THE PARTIES WERE MET THEMSELVES,
ONE OF THEM THOUGHT BUT OF AN 'IF': . . . AND THEY SHOOK
HANDS, AND SWORE BROTHERS. YOUR 'IF' IS THE ONLY
PEACE-MAKER; MUCH VIRTUE IN 'IF'."   WILLIAM SHAKESPEARE
"AS YOU LIKE IT"   ACT V   SCENE IV   (TOUCHSTONE)

9.1   INSTANCES WHEN INTERACTIONS DO NOT PROVIDE A SUITABLE PARTITION

Nothing in partitioning is mechanical; it follows that there are times when a factorial partition is not appropriate even though the treatments form a factorial set. Suppose, for example, that a drug has been evolved; it is known to have antipyretic properties, and the question arises as to which conditions it will benefit. There are a number of reasons why a patient's temperature may be raised, and an experimenter might well take patients representing, say, four conditions, and administer the drug to half in each group. The treatment sum of squares could then be partitioned thus:

Conditions (C)	3
Drug (D)	1
$C \times D$	3

However, no interest attaches to the interaction, because the experimenter does not expect the drug to be equally beneficial in all conditions. If he assumes that it might well reduce temperature in some circumstances but not necessarily in others, he may prefer to partition thus:

Conditions	3
Drug in condition W	1
Drug in condition X	1
Drug in condition Y	1
Drug in condition Z	1

The four single degrees of freedom and their sums of squared deviations will then tell him whether the drug is effective as an antipyretic or not

140

in each of the four conditions taken separately. In these circumstances, in which the existence of an interaction is virtually being assumed, the main effect of conditions is without meaning.

Another instance where the usual partition into main effects and interactions may be unhelpful arises when the factors are alternatives. Thus, it may be suspected that the application of either hormone A or B will inhibit growth, the two together being no more effective than either singly. Consider, for example, these figures, where each is supposed to be the total growth on five plots.

	No A	A
No B	140	103
B	97	101

Such a reaction inflates the mean squares for the interaction and for the two main effects to about the same degree. Thus, the treatment sum of squares equals 239.75, of which 54.45 belongs to the main effect of A, 101.25 to the main effect of B, and 84.05 to the interaction. In fact the real difference, that between no hormone and hormone, could easily be missed on account of its being dispersed over the 3 degrees of freedom. If such a result were expected, it would be better to partition thus:

No hormone v. hormone   1
Between hormone treatments   2

The 2 degrees of freedom would be studied first. If it should appear that the three hormone treatments did not form a homogeneous group, it would make no sense to compare them collectively with the other treatment.

The single degree of freedom corresponds to the contrast $\{3, \ -1, -1, \ -1\}$, which has the sum of squares

$$\frac{[3(140) - 103 - 97 - 101]^2}{5 \times 12}$$

This comes to 236.02 or almost the whole of the sum of squared deviations for treatments.

The sum of squared deviations for the 2 degrees of freedom can be obtained in two ways. The more obvious is to work out

$$\frac{103^2 + 97^2 + 101^2}{5} - \frac{301^2}{15} = 3.73$$

An easier way is to take each degree of freedom separately and then to add the results. It does not matter how the further partition is effected, since the results are to be combined, but one way is to take the contrasts {0,   1,   1,   −2} and {0,   1,   −1,   0}, which give sums of squares respectively equal to 0.13 and 3.60, or 3.73 in all, as before.

Such a partition is like any other; it is valid only if it expresses the experimenter's thoughts.

9.2   A NUMERICAL EXAMPLE INVOLVING INTERACTIONS

An example of the practical aspects of interpreting interactions is afforded by an experiment done in the later stages of the investigation into the effect of growth substances upon peas. Doses of 1, 10, and 100 micrograms of gibberellic acid were applied to nodes 3, 6, and 9, and measurement made of the thickness of leaf at node 10, the data being those given in Table 9.1.

Table 9.1
Data from a 3^2 factorial experiment on dose and position of application of gibberellic acid

Treatment	Block				
	I	II	III	IV	
00	9.0	8.9	9.1	9.0	36.0
01	7.6	8.1	9.3	7.2	32.2
02	7.1	8.3	8.3	8.0	31.7
10	6.6	6.5	9.2	8.9	31.2
11	6.0	5.6	7.0	6.3	24.9
12	8.7	9.0	8.5	8.3	34.5
20	6.7	8.8	6.5	7.0	29.0
21	5.9	5.8	6.4	5.9	24.0
22	9.1	7.8	9.0	7.0	32.9
	66.7	68.8	73.3	67.6	276.4

In the coding of the treatments the first digit represents the dose (0=1, 1 = 10, 2 = 100) and the second the node (0 = 3, 1 = 6, 2 = 9). The factors will be called D (for dose) and N (for node).

The treatment combinations are written in a square, as in Table 9.2.

Table 9.2
Total for each treatment combination of the
data in Table 9.1

	D_0	D_1	D_2	
N_0	36.0	31.2	29.0	96.2
N_1	32.2	24.9	24.0	81.1
N_2	31.7	34.5	32.9	99.1
	99.9	90.6	85.9	276.4

Hence the summation terms are:

T	2 172.9000
T_1	2 124.9978
T_{DN}	2 155.2100
T_D	2 130.5983
T_N	2 137.7050
T_0	2 122.1378

These lead to the analysis given in Table 9.3.

Table 9.3
Analysis of variance for the data in Table 9.1

Source	df	Sum of squares	Mean square	F
Blocks	3	2.8600		
D	2	8.4605	4.2303	6.85**
N	2	15.5672	7.7836	12.60***
D × N	4	9.0445	2.2611	3.66*
Error	24	14.8300	0.6179	
Total	35	50.7622		

To consider now the interpretation of the analysis, the significance
($P < 0.05$) of the interaction gives warning that the effects of dose and of
node number should not be considered in isolation from one another. In fact,
examination of the nine treatment totals shows clearly what has happened.
The application of gibberellic acid to node 6 has had the effect of making the
leaves at node 10 thinner. Applied to node 9, it has had no effect, possibly
because there has not been time for the substance to act. Applied at node 3

the effect is much as at node 6, though it has perhaps partly worn off. Also, at nodes 3 and 6, the greater the dose, the greater the effect. These conclusions contain substantially all the information to be gleaned from the experiment.

It would, however, be more systematic to argue thus: There is an interaction; therefore no rash generalizations ought to be made about the effect of either dose or number of the treated node. Accordingly, the effect of dose needs to be studied for each node number in turn; the result of this partition is that shown in Table 9.4.

Table 9.4
Alternative partition of the treatment sum of squared
deviations in Table 9.3

Source	df	Sum of squares	F
D(linear) at N_0	1	6.1250	9.91**
D(parabolic) at N_0	1	0.2817	
D(linear) at N_1	1	8.4050	13.60**
D(parabolic) at N_1	1	1.7067	2.76
D(linear) at N_2	1	0.1800	
D(parabolic) at N_2	1	0.8067	1.31
$D + (D \times N)$	6	17.5050	

This indicates the effect of dose for each node. For node 9 there is no apparent effect, for node 6 a large one, and for node 3 a smaller one. Further, all response curves appear to be straight, the doses being equally spaced on a logarithmic scale.

To be strictly systematic an experimenter should then look at the differences between nodes for each dose, though this is less natural than the partition just given. In some contexts, however, one could be as reasonable as the other. The result of the fresh partition is that shown in Table 9.5. The interpretation is not as obvious as before; the conclusion is that at the low dose there is little difference between the nodes; at the middle dose, nodes 3 and 9 are much the same but node 6 is markedly different; at the high dose, the same differences appear but to a smaller degree. After these two subsidiary partitions, both of which are suggested by the existence of an interaction, an experimenter could reasonably feel that he had studied the data adequately, indeed exhaustively.

Table 9.5
Further possible partition of the treatment sum of squared
deviations in Table 9.3

Source	df	Sum of squares	F
N(linear) at D_0	1	2.3113	3.74
N(parabolic) at D_0	1	0.4538	
N(linear) at D_1	1	1.3613	2.20
N(parabolic) at D_1	1	10.5338	17.05***
N(linear) at D_2	1	1.9013	3.07
N(parabolic) at D_2	1	8.0504	13.03**
$N + (D \times N)$	6	24.6117	

9.3   SOME SPECIAL CASES

If all factors are at two levels, a simplified method of computing the components of the treatment sum of squared deviations becomes possible. Indeed, it has already been indicated for the case of the lamb-feeding experiment. This had 2^2 treatments, and it was pointed out that the main effects corresponded to the partitions

$$\{1, \quad 1, \quad -1, \quad -1\}$$
and $$\{1, \quad -1, \quad 1, \quad -1\}$$

and the interaction to

$$\{1, \quad -1, \quad -1, \quad 1\}$$

This approach is readily generalized. Suppose that there are four factors, W, X, Y, and Z; then there will be 16 treatment combinations, namely, O, W, X, Y, Z, WX, WY, WZ, XY, XZ, YZ, WXY, WXZ, WYZ, XYZ, and $WXYZ$. Suppose now that the interaction of $W \times Y \times Z$ is required. The 16 treatments are divided into two groups, one containing those in which W, Y, and Z occur an odd number of times, and the other, those in which their number of occurrences is even. (Thus, XY, Z, and WYZ belong to the first class and YZ, WYZ, and 0 to the second.) The contrast between these two groups gives the required interaction, namely,

$$\{1, \quad -1, \quad 1, \quad -1, \quad -1, \quad -1, \quad 1, \quad 1, \quad -1, \quad -1, \quad 1, \quad 1, \quad 1,$$
$$-1, \quad 1, \quad -1\}$$

This provides a very easy way of calculating the sum of squared deviations for any interaction, especially as the divisor for the contrast always equals the total number of plots in the experiment.

Where all factors are at three levels, another simplified method exists. The treatment combinations can be represented by two-digit numbers, the first digit being 0, 1, or 2 according to the level of the first factor, and the second digit assuming similar values according to the levels of the second. The nine treatment totals can now be thought of in a square, thus:

(00)   (01)   (02)
(10)   (11)   (12)
(20)   (21)   (22)

If now these values are summed horizontally, totals for the three levels of the first factor will be obtained. A summation term, T_X, can be derived from them. Similarly, vertical summing will do the same for the second factor, Y. Now the totals are summed down diagonals, starting from the top left-hand corner, to give the "I totals," thus:

I_1 = total of 00, 11, and 22
I_2 = total of 10, 21, and 02
I_3 = total of 20, 01, and 12

A summation term, T_1, may be obtained from these quantities also; similarly T_J may be obtained by summing the diagonals that go the other way, i.e.,

J_1 = total of 00, 21, and 12
J_2 = total of 10, 01, and 22
J_3 = total of 20, 11, and 02

It will then be found that the 4 degrees of freedom for the interaction equal $T_I + T_J - 2T_0$. Thus, in the example of the different doses of gibberellic acid applied to different nodes,

$I_1 = 93.8,\quad I_2 = 95.7,\quad I_3 = 86.9$
$J_1 = 94.5,\quad J_2 = 96.3,\quad J_3 = 85.6$

Therefore

$T_I = 2\ 125.7117$
$T_J = 2\ 127.6083$

and $T_I + T_J - 2T_0 = 9.0444$, which is indeed the interaction sum of squares apart from a rounding-off error. It is true that this method of calculation has no practical advantage, but it will prove to be important later, revealing as it does a useful property of a 3×3 interaction.

This method can be extended to higher-order interactions. Thus, suppose there are three factors, A, B, and C, each at three levels; then it is possible to work out values of I_1, I_2, I_3, J_1, J_2, and J_3, for A and B at each level of C. If now the nine I values so obtained are arranged in a square, rows representing I_1, I_2, and I_3, and columns, C_0, C_1, and C_2, and if diagonals are summed from the top left-hand corner, the three totals that result are the W values. Taking diagonals the other way gives the X values. Repeating with J, instead of I, values gives respectively the Y and Z values. It appears that the sum of squares for the interaction $A \times B \times C$ can be found as the sum of four components, each with 2 degrees of freedom, namely $(T_W - T_0)$, $(T_X - T_0)$, $(T_Y - T_0)$, and $(T_Z - T_0)$, i.e., the sum of squares for the interaction equals $(T_W + T_X + T_Y + T_Z - 4T_0)$ with 8 degrees of freedom. Again the property is of little importance in itself, but it has useful consequences.

9.4   CONFOUNDING

With split-plot designs the analysis is carried out in two parts. Because the *first* part refers to *main* plots, it sounds the more important, but it is really the second that is the chief part, because it is the more sensitive. Indeed, contrasts in the first part can be thought of as relegated to a limbo of the unimportant. Many instances occur in which there is little point in computing the first part at all, either because it is so insensitive that it can hardly be expected to show anything, or because the contrasts in it are of such little interest. In such instances these contrasts are said to be "confounded."

The confounding of interactions is no more difficult. Like the use of split plots it enables the block size to be reduced, possibly improving the comparison of the contrasts that remain. Since very high-order interactions often elude interpretation anyway, their loss does little harm. On the other hand, nothing is to be gained unless the smaller block size facilitated by the confounding does lead to a reduced estimate of error.

The method may be illustrated by considering a 2^3 factorial design with factors X, Y, and Z. The treatment combinations are therefore O, X, Y, Z, XY, XZ, YZ, XYZ. The main effect of X is given by the contrast of the groups O, Y, Z, YZ and X, XY, XZ, XYZ. If half the blocks have one group and half have the other, the result is obviously a split-plot design, i.e., the main effect of X has been confounded. Suppose, however, that the interaction $X \times Z$ had been taken instead. This time half the blocks would have O, Y, XZ, XYZ and half would have X, Z, XY, YZ; the essential principle is the same. Further, it would still be possible to carry out a subsidiary analysis, separating out the difference between those blocks having one group and those having the other, the remaining degrees of freedom between blocks being assigned to Error i. Apart from nomenclature ("blocks" corresponding to "main plots" in a split-plot design; "plots" to "subplots"; and the "subsidiary" analysis to the "first" analysis), everything is as for a split-plot design except that the contrast which is less well compared is an interaction instead of a main effect.

Similarly, if there were two factors each at three levels, it would be possible to associate I_1 with one third of the blocks, I_2 with another third, and I_3 with the remainder—or the same could be done with the J component of the interaction. Equally, if there were three factors each at three levels, it would be possible to treat one of the W, X, Y, or Z components similarly.

Where an interaction or one of its components is confounded, the whole interaction is omitted from the analysis. This sometimes leads to the question of what happens if the confounded interaction is in fact important. Its omission does nothing to alter the significance or nonsignificance of the main effects and interactions that remain. On the other hand, a significant interaction can affect the interpretation placed on interactions and main effects contained within it. Therefore, if its significance cannot be gauged, a faulty interpretation might result. Accordingly, it is wise to confound only interactions that are most unlikely to be significant or those whose significance can be assumed. An alternative course is to recover the interaction in a main-plot analysis as is done in split-plot designs when a main effect is confounded.

In any experiment where there are many factors, it is permissible to pool some of the high-order interactions with error. This also leads to questioning, but in a multifactorial experiment interactions of the highest order are often so complicated as to defy reasonable interpretation, and it may not be felt useful to keep them separate. If they are pooled with error, more degrees of freedom for error are obtained at the risk of inflating the error sum of squares if one of the discarded interactions really does have an effect. Where an interaction can be pooled with error, no harm is done by confounding it instead. On the other hand, confounding, if it can be done, makes possible smaller blocks, and this might reduce the standard deviation considerably.

CHAPTER TEN

CORRELATION
AND REGRESSION

SO FAR VARIABLE QUANTITIES HAVE BEEN
THOUGHT OF IN ISOLATION, BUT OFTEN ONE
WANTS TO LEARN HOW CLOSELY THEY ARE
RELATED AND IN WHAT WAY.

. . . IN SICILY, THIGH-BONES AND SHOULDER-BONES HAVE BEEN
FOUND OF SO IMMENSE A SIZE, THAT FROM THENCE OF
NECESSITY WE MUST CONCLUDE BY THE CERTAIN RULES OF
GEOMETRY, THAT THE MEN TO WHOM THEY BELONGED WERE
GIANTS, AS BIG AS HUGE STEEPLES.   MIGUEL DE CERVANTES
"THE HISTORY OF DON QUIXOTE DE LA MANCHA"
PART II CHAPTER I

So far one variate has been analyzed at a time, but this is not a situation that will appeal to the biologist, who by his training thinks in terms of relationships within organisms rather than of measurements in isolation. Indeed, there is perhaps no more potent source of misunderstanding between statistician and biologist than the tendency of the one to think in univariate terms and the other in multivariate, without the difference ever being perceived. In this chapter a start will be made on the task of considering variates in their relationship to one another.

10.1   CORRELATION COEFFICIENTS

The basic inquiry about any two variates is whether they are related or not, and here it is usual to employ a method that originated with Galton, the associate of Charles Darwin. Suppose that there are two columns of figures representing corresponding values of two variates, x and y. The inquiry concerns the degree of association between them. Galton's method was to consider each variate separately and work out deviations from the mean. If now there is a tendency for high values of one variate to be associated with high values of the other, and also for low values to occur together, the deviations of the two variates will usually be of the same sign, and most of the products of deviations will be positive. On the other hand, if an increase in one is associated with a decrease in the other, most of the products of deviations will be negative, as in Table 10.1.

In fact, the basis of Galton's "correlation coefficient" is a sum of products of deviations. This is analogous to the sum of squared deviations

150

Table 10.1
Example of a sum of products of deviations

Data		Deviations		Product
x	y	x	y	
14	9	0	−2	0
17	8	3	−3	−9
11	15	−3	4	−12
10	14	−4	3	−12
15	12	1	1	+1
19	8	3	−3	−9
Total	84	66	0	0	−41
Mean	14	11			

already used for measuring the variation of single variates. Further, it may be calculated in a similar way, first multiplying together pairs of data to produce a total summation term and then multiplying together the totals and dividing by the number of pairs of data to produce a correction summation term. Thus, in this example, the sum of products of deviations, which will be written C_{xy}, equals

$$(14 \times 9) + (17 \times 8) + (11 \times 15) + (10 \times 14) + (15 \times 12)$$
$$+ (17 \times 8) - \tfrac{1}{6}(84 \times 66) = 883 - 924 = -41$$

It will be seen that a sum of products, unlike a sum of squares, can be negative.

However, such a quantity is dependent upon the units of measurement of the variates. Thus, if y were measured in centimeters instead of meters, the sum of products would be increased one-hundred times. Accordingly, it is scaled by the square roots of the sums of squares, which here are 44 for x and 48 for y. The coefficient of correlation, which is usually written r, therefore equals $-41/\sqrt{44 \times 48}$ or about -0.9.

The limits of r are ± 1. It equals $+1$ only when changes in one variate are associated with changes in the other that are exactly proportionate and in the same direction. If changes are proportionate but in opposite directions, r equals -1. If a change in one does not indicate a change in the other, r equals zero.

Two points need to be noticed. One is that the existence of a marked correlation coefficient does not necessarily prove causation, least of all when observations are made over a period of time. Thus, during the last three decades in Britain there has been an increase in juvenile delinquency and a decline in the incidence of tuberculosis, but it would be foolish to argue that either must be the cause of the other. It would, however, be equally foolish to deny the existence of a correlation between them; this is real enough although not causative in nature.

Also, the absence of correlation does not mean that there is no association of any kind, only that it is not in the form of a trend common to the two variates. Thus, if y falls to a minimum with increasing x and then rises again, the two limbs of the curve could cancel one another out, as in the admittedly artificial example of Table 10.2.

Table 10.2
Example of uncorrelated but
associated variates

Data		Deviations		Product
x	y	x	y	
1	50	−3	12	−36
2	40	−2	2	−4
3	30	−1	−8	8
4	26	0	−12	0
5	30	1	−8	−8
6	40	2	2	4
7	50	3	12	36
Total 28	266	0	0	0
Mean 4	38			

The significance of a correlation coefficient is easily judged. Tables can be used (Fisher and Yates, Table VI), or use can be made of the analysis of variance. If the sums of squared deviations for x and y are written C_{xx} and C_{yy}, respectively, and the sum of products of deviations is written C_{xy}, then the correlation coefficient, r, equals $C_{xy}/\sqrt{C_{xx}C_{yy}}$. Moreover, that part of the variation in y that can be accounted for by the action of x can be shown to equal $C_{yy}r^2$. It is this that makes an analysis of variance possible. If no account is taken of the action of x, the sum of squared deviations for y is C_{yy}, with, say, f degrees of freedom. If, however, account is taken of x, the variation in y still unexplained is $C_{yy}(1 - r^2)$, which has $(f - 1)$ degrees of freedom, so the analysis of variance is

Source	df	Sum of squares
Correlation	1	$C_{yy}r^2$
Error	$f - 1$	$C_{yy}(1 - r^2)$
Total	f	C_{yy}

An F test will show whether the correlation can or cannot be attributed to chance. The same conclusion would have been reached if the position of the variates had been reversed and attention had been directed to the variation in x and the extent to which it could be explained by the variation in y.

10.2   CONFLICTING   CORRELATIONS

It has already been pointed out that a significant correlation coefficient is not necessarily evidence of causation; equally, a small coefficient can arise when there are two marked functional relationships if they operate in opposition to one another. For example, broadly speaking there are two ways of obtaining more fruit from an apple tree. One is to make the tree grow larger, the other is to inhibit growth so that the tree's efforts are diverted into fruiting. The intensive methods of cultivation in peasant communities exemplify both approaches: the trees are heavily fertilized, but planted at an angle or bent horizontal to retard growth. Is growth correlated negatively or positively with fruiting? The answer must depend on the nature of the stimulus that has been applied. If some trees are on better soil or have more moisture, the correlation will be positive, whereas if they differ because some are more crowded than others, those that have to struggle more to extend to find the light can be expected to bear less weight of fruit. According to circumstances, the correlation coefficient could have almost any value.

Many other examples can be thought of where two variates can be associated in conflicting ways. Thus a pupil who excels at geography may be of high intelligence and therefore better than average at mathematics. Alternatively, he may find geography interesting and give too much time to it, this leading to poor results in mathematics. A man may lack sufficient bread to eat, this leading to his being underweight; another may eat so many attractive foods that he scarcely ever touches bread and this leads to his being overweight. What is the correlation?

It can therefore be very dangerous to elevate a correlation coefficient to the expression of a law of nature. Another investigator might induce differences by other means so that the coefficient changes sign or disappears. Of course some relations are fixed, but they are mostly trivial like that between the volumes and weights of pieces of lead. In biology they are rarely so simple, and too many people have established "laws" without specifying the stimuli that are assumed to be acting. This is of special relevance with one common use of correlation coefficients. Within a set of plants or animals similarly treated, it may be observed that x, which is important but difficult to measure, is highly correlated with y, which is unimportant but easy to measure. Someone then suggests that in the future y should be measured instead of x because "it comes to the same thing." Within a similarly treated set this may be true, but the whole point of an experiment is that plots are treated differently. If the treatments are different in nature from the error, the relation between x and y may be quite different between treatments from what it was within them.

10.3 THREE VARIATES

As has been said, an association between two variates is not evidence of causation; sometimes it results from common causation, both variates being affected by a third. It is said that there is a strong positive correlation between the number of ministers of religion in a town and the consumption of gin. Probably there is, because both reflect the town's population.

It is sometimes loosely said that there is no "real" correlation in such cases, but this is not true. What the third variate has done is to cast doubt on the extent to which the correlation between the other two is causative, but a wise investigator would have had doubts anyway.

Nevertheless, the case of three variates merits attention. Let them be w, x, and y, and let the sums of squared deviations be C_{ww}, C_{xx}, and C_{yy}, respectively, and let the three sums of products of deviations be C_{xy}, C_{wy}, and C_{wx}. The correlation coefficient between x and y is $C_{xy}/\sqrt{C_{xx}C_{yy}}$ and will be written r_{xy}. If now the effect of w on both x and y is eliminated, the correlation coefficient between them becomes

$$\frac{C_{xy}C_{ww} - C_{wx}C_{wy}}{\sqrt{(C_{ww}C_{yy} - C_{wy}^2)(C_{ww}C_{xx} - C_{wx}^2)}} = \frac{r_{xy} - r_{wx}r_{wy}}{\sqrt{(1 - r_{wx}^2)(1 - r_{wy}^2)}}$$

This is written $r_{xy \cdot w}$ and is called a "partial correlation coefficient." It will be seen that if w is correlated with neither x nor y, i.e., $r_{wx} = 0 = r_{wy}$, then $r_{xy \cdot w} = r_{xy}$, which is quite reasonable.

To illustrate the case of three variates by a numerical example, the writer some time ago was investigating ways of measuring the weight of a plum tree without damaging it. One possibility was to pull up a group of mature trees, weigh each one, and see how far a relationship could be established with the trunk circumferences. It was decided to use all measurements in logarithmic transformation because experience had shown that log (tree weight) plotted against log (trunk circumference) usually gave a straight-line relationship. Of course, logarithms of size show up growth rates, and it is not surprising that a tree with a fast-growing trunk should have a proportionately fast-increasing weight.

The three variates were:

w, log (circumference at the base of the trunk)
x, log (circumference at the top of the trunk)
y, log (weight of tree above ground)

Table 10.3
Size data for plum trees grown on four kinds of roots

Own Roots			Common Plum		
w	x	y	w	x	y
1.690	1.663	2.318	1.525	1.515	1.940
1.583	1.568	2.100	1.517	1.501	1.940
1.693	1.643	2.225	1.582	1.542	2.045
1.648	1.609	2.140	1.537	1.529	1.919
1.628	1.599	2.107	1.504	1.487	1.869
1.600	1.603	2.049	1.589	1.562	2.049
1.677	1.640	2.228	1.567	1.548	1.954
1.588	1.535	2.029	1.480	1.449	1.820
1.645	1.606	2.140	1.498	1.490	1.892
14.752	14.466	19.336	13.799	13.623	17.428
Common Mussel			Myrobalan B		
w	x	y	w	x	y
1.604	1.540	2.104	1.747	1.712	2.382
1.650	1.633	2.233	1.769	1.754	2.413
1.591	1.581	2.090	1.763	1.747	2.446
1.598	1.579	2.079	1.766	1.738	2.450
1.672	1.629	2.255	1.739	1.719	2.387
1.585	1.555	2.064	1.749	1.742	2.396
1.645	1.610	2.185	1.738	1.710	2.310
1.628	1.612	2.068	1.731	1.689	2.332
1.653	1.642	2.201	1.707	1.650	2.204
14.626	14.381	19.279	15.709	15.461	21.320

w = log (circumference at base of trunk)
x = log (circumference at top of trunk)
y = log (weight of tree above ground)

Data were available from thirty-six trees of the variety Pershore Egg. Nine were growing on their own roots, nine were grafted on Common Plum, nine on Common Mussel, and nine on Myrobalan B. The data are shown in Table 10.3.

Before proceeding further it is important to decide what sort of variation is under study. Thus, it is conceivable that between rootstocks, trees that give a large trunk will give a low weight, though between trees on the same rootstock the two quantities were positively correlated. Examination shows that so extreme a situation does not arise here, but a warning has already been given that differences in a variate may lead to different effects in another variate according to the cause of the change. Here the interest centers on the variation of trees within rootstocks; accordingly use will be made of sums of squares and products, each with 32 degrees of freedom, obtained as the difference of the total and the rootstock summation terms.

Because at a later stage the rootstocks will be considered in isolation, the sums of squares and products will here be obtained each as the sum of four components, one for each rootstock, each with 8 degrees of freedom. This will give the same ultimate answer, but it will be more trouble, so it would be adopted only in circumstances where the calculation might need to be reworked in more detail later.

Own Roots

$$C_{ww} = 0.014\ 457 \quad C_{xx} = 0.012\ 310 \quad C_{yy} = 0.069\ 302$$
$$C_{xy} = 0.026\ 087 \quad C_{wy} = 0.028\ 817 \quad C_{wx} = 0.012\ 166$$

Common Plum

$$C_{ww} = 0.011\ 904 \quad C_{xx} = 0.010\ 168 \quad C_{yy} = 0.045\ 174$$
$$C_{xy} = 0.019\ 191 \quad C_{wy} = 0.021\ 747 \quad C_{wx} = 0.010\ 545$$

Common Mussel

$$C_{ww} = 0.007\ 953 \quad C_{xx} = 0.010\ 325 \quad C_{yy} = 0.046\ 057$$
$$C_{xy} = 0.016\ 403 \quad C_{wy} = 0.017\ 263 \quad C_{wx} = 0.007\ 875$$

Myrobalan B

$$C_{ww} = 0.003\ 084 \quad C_{xx} = 0.008\ 679 \quad C_{yy} = 0.047\ 723$$
$$C_{xy} = 0.018\ 790 \quad C_{wy} = 0.011\ 370 \quad C_{wx} = 0.004\ 930$$

Adding the four components together, which for the moment is what is needed,

$$C_{ww} = 0.037\ 398 \quad C_{xx} = 0.041\ 482 \quad C_{yy} = 0.208\ 256$$
$$C_{xy} = 0.080\ 471 \quad C_{wy} = 0.079\ 197 \quad C_{wx} = 0.035\ 516$$

Usually eight decimal places would have been taken in each of these sums of squares and products, because the data are given to three places. However the last place in the data was doubtful, so only six places were taken here.

Hence

$$r_{xy} = +0.8658$$
$$r_{wy} = +0.8974$$
$$r_{wx} = +0.9017$$

Although by most standards these correlation coefficients are high, they are smaller than those often encountered in this sort of work.

Ordinarily two decimal places suffice for correlation coefficients, but these are to be used in further calculations so more have been taken.

The question now arises how far y, the logarithm of tree weights, is related to w and x, the logarithms of the trunk circumferences; here the partial correlation coefficients may help. Thus

$$r_{xy \cdot w} = \frac{r_{xy} - r_{wx} r_{wy}}{\sqrt{(1 - r_{wx}^2)(1 - r_{wy}^2)}} = +0.30$$

From this it might appear that the weight is associated with the upper circumference chiefly because both are associated with the lower. However, $r_{wy \cdot x}$ is not large either. It is

$$\frac{r_{wy} - r_{wx} r_{xy}}{\sqrt{(1 - r_{wx}^2)(1 - r_{xy}^2)}} = +0.53$$

What these results show is that a person who is seeking to estimate y can do so effectively if he knows either w or x. If he knows one of them, he will not be much helped by knowing the other as well. Again correlation coefficients have served for descriptive purposes only; they do not necessarily reveal laws of nature.

In this instance the sum of squares for y was 0.208 256. Of this,

$$\frac{C_{wy}(C_{wy}C_{xx} - C_{wx}C_{xy}) + C_{xy}(C_{ww}C_{xy} - C_{wx}C_{wy})}{(C_{ww}C_{xx} - C_{wx}^2)}$$

= 0.171 282 with 2 degrees of freedom may be attributed to the correlations. To the correlation with w, $C_{wy}^2/C_{ww} = 0.167\,714$ belongs; to the correlation with x, $C_{xy}^2/C_{xx} = 0.156\,106$, each with 1 degree of freedom. Hence the analysis of variance in Table 10.4 can be drawn up.

Table 10.4

Analysis of variance for correlations of one variate, y, with two
others, w and x

Source	df	Sum of squares
Correlation with w alone	1	0.167 714
Partial correlation with x	1	0.003 568
Correlation with x alone	1	0.156 106
Partial correlation with w	1	0.015 176
Multiple correlation with w and x	2	0.171 282
Error	30	0.036 974
Total	32	0.208 256

With two variates, that part of the variation C_{yy} in y that can be
attributed to x is $C_{yy}r^2$. Here, where there are three variates, that part of the
variation in y that can be attributed to w and x is $C_{yy}R^2$, where R is called a
"multiple correlation coefficient." Here $R^2 = 0.171\ 282/0.208\ 256$, so R
equals 0.91, the sign being always taken as positive.

From F tests it appears that correlations of y with w and x are very
highly significant ($P < 0.001$). There is no reason to attach any importance
to the partial correlations with x, but it appears that w adds something to the
knowledge of y derived from x alone.

There is no reason why this process should end at three variates. Thus,
if there are four, the partial correlation between x and y, eliminating the
effects of v and w, may be written $r_{xy \cdot vw}$. It equals

$$\frac{r_{xy \cdot w} - r_{vx \cdot w} r_{vy \cdot w}}{\sqrt{(1 - r_{vx \cdot w}^2)(1 - r_{vy \cdot w}^2)}}$$

an expression analogous to that for $r_{xy \cdot w}$ in terms of r_{xy} and r_{wy}. However,
the formulas for the sum of squares corresponding to each higher-order
partial correlation coefficient can be quite complicated and will not be discussed here.

10.4   SURVEYS AND EXPERIMENTS

On being introduced to correlation methods, most people feel that they have
acquired a tool of immense value for studying complex situations. After a

large output of effort many of them then adopt the opposite attitude and assert that the methods are of no use at all. In fact, they are of use, but only in a limited range of circumstances.

It has already been emphasized that association is not the same as causation. Thus, a number of variates may all be correlated among themselves, but no one can say from inspection of data which is the one that pulls the trigger, as it were. An example has just been presented in which there are two trunk circumferences, both of which are highly correlated with the tree weight. In fact, there is reason to think that weight depends chiefly on the area of the top of the trunk because it is this that determines the basal area of the branches. There is, perhaps, some hint of this in the correlation coefficients, but no one could have inferred much of the mechanism of the effect from the figures given.

The only way to elucidate causation effects is to vary related factors separately, but how does one grow a tree in which the top of the trunk is of different circumference from the bottom? As it happens, this can be done by using different rootstocks, but without such a device the two variates would have remained inextricably associated. As long as one variate cannot be altered without altering the other, there is no need to ask which of them affects tree weight. Nevertheless, an experimenter may well harbor doubts about what would happen if in some unforeseen circumstances his advice to estimate a from b was falsified because a third variate c ceased to be associated with b, and it turned out that really it was c and not b that had the effect on a.

This doubt lies at the base of much of the skepticism about surveys as a substitute for experiments. At first sight it is easy to avoid the labor of a controlled experiment by noting what happens in uncontrolled natural conditions, but further consideration leads to the realization that the natural association of variates can mislead. Thus, an inept investigator might note that tuberculosis was more rife in families that lacked a proper bathroom and then conclude from this that the provision of bathrooms at schools would reduce the incidence of tuberculosis among young people. It would be more reasonable to conclude that families in poor circumstances lack bathrooms, adequate sleeping space, and good food. He would then see that this was one further piece of evidence connecting malnutrition and overcrowding with tuberculosis. Again, an agricultural economist might observe that farmers who employed little labor rarely made a profit. If he confined himself to a recommendation to avoid the false economy of understaffing a farm, he might well be right. There is, however, nothing to be said for employing more men if the farmer has no idea what they could usefully do. Again, the outcome, profitable farming, depends upon a complex of factors, labor costs being only one of them. As long as all factors of the complex change together, there is no reason to choose one as the operative cause. To change one without making all the concomitant changes could be ineffective or even disastrous.

This is a danger in any conclusion based on a survey. It is especially likely in biological work where the study is of an organism such that any part might affect any other part.

Even if an experiment is performed, there is the risk of obscuring the issue by unnoticed concomitant changes. Thus, a report appeared recently in which the head of an orphanage explained that when he took up his post the children had been apathetic and uncooperative. He had therefore tried an experiment. Whenever a child had a birthday, he was called out from the group, shaken by the hand, and given a small present. At the end of a year, the report said, the attitude of the children was so changed that the advisability of giving birthday presents had been amply demonstrated. It may, however, be suggested that the reason for the children acquiring a sense of their own dignity was a change in the attitude of those responsible for them, the giving of birthday presents being only one factor in a complex of changes brought about by a good head. Though the most spectacular, it may have been the least important. As an experiment, the weakness was not the lack of replication or randomization, but a failure to specify the treatments.

In practice, any experimenter has to consider how far he does wish to dissociate his treatments from their natural concomitants. If the administration of a certain drug requires that the patient shall rest, no one would suggest administering it otherwise, though a cynic might suggest telling some patients to rest and seeing if that explained the observed benefit.

Basically one difference is this—in an experiment a good investigator can contrive to test a treatment in conjunction with such concomitants as he chooses. In a survey there is always the risk of including unwanted ones. In general, this risk is present whenever correlation coefficients are used. There is no better way of describing association phenomena; their scientific interpretation is often dubious.

10.5   REGRESSION COEFFICIENTS

As has been explained, correlation relates to the degree of association between variates, not with the way in which they relate. In fact, a correlation coefficient is calculated assuming that two variates are subject to steady trends relative to each other, and this assumption enters also into the calculation of partial correlation coefficients; where two variates are adjusted by a third, the adjustment is made assuming a straight-line relationship between any pair of variates. Nevertheless, though relationships have of necessity been assumed, the object has been to study the *intensity* of association. In regression the *form* of relationship is considered.

Suppose, to begin with, that the relationship is of the kind assumed in the last chapter, a change in x being associated with a proportionate change in y, whether in the same direction or opposite to it. In fact, let

$$Y = a + bx$$

where Y is the estimate that will be made of y when x takes any given value.

It will be seen that x and y are no longer in a symmetrical relationship to one another. As far as correlations are concerned, x is as highly correlated with y as y is with x; here, however, x takes up some value, and the problem is to decide what value is to be expected of y. To mark the different statuses, x is said to be the "independent" variate and y the "dependent" one. Some have preferred to call them the "affecting" and the "affected" variates respectively. Here the former nomenclature will be employed because it is more established and commoner.

The quantity b is of some importance. It is called the "regression coefficient" and it indicates the change to be expected in y if x alters by one.

It is not difficult to show mathematically that if x takes up its mean value, $\bar{x}$, Y can be expected to equal the mean of the y data, that is, $\bar{y}$. Thus, in the example of the trunk circumferences and tree weights, if a tree should have average log (upper circumference), that is, $x = 1.607$ for trees on their own roots, then it can be expected to have a value of log (tree weight) equal to 2.148, that being the corresponding mean. Actually, there is no tree on its own roots for which $x = 1.607$, but there is one for which $x = 1.609$ and $y = 2.140$, which shows quite good agreement with what has just been said. Hence, in general,

$$(Y - \bar{y}) = b(x - \bar{x})$$

It can also be shown that b is best estimated as $C_{xy}/C_{xx} = 1.940$, so

$$(Y - 2.140) = 1.940(x - 1.607)$$
or $\qquad Y = -0.978 + 1.940x$

The significance of b is the same as that of r, to which it is related. Also, $C_{yy}(1 - r^2) = C_{yy} - C_{xy}^2/C_{xx}$, which has $(f - 1)$ degrees of freedom, represents the extent to which the actual values of y differ from the expected values, Y. It is, in fact, an estimate of error, the effect of the regression having been taken into account. This quantity has already been considered.

As has been said, x and y have different roles. It is, moreover, quite feasible to imagine them reversed, an experimenter knowing the value of y and wanting an estimate, X, of the other variate. Plainly, by a modification of the formulas already given,

$$(X - \bar{x}) = b'(y - \bar{y})$$

where
$$b' = \frac{C_{xy}}{C_{yy}}$$

so
$$X = 0.781 + 0.386y$$

Graphing these two regression lines, that of Y against x and that of X against y, it will be seen that they are not the same. If x and y were completely associated, that is, $r = \pm 1$, so that neither was affected by any factor except the other, then indeed there would be one single line corresponding to the law that associated them. (Even this state of affairs could arise only if the relationship was expressible by a straight line.) In general, however, each variate is affected not only by the other, but by disturbing factors, so the lines lie a little apart. Indeed, in the extreme case where x and y are quite independent, Y equals $\bar{y}$ regardless of x, and X equals $\bar{x}$ regardless of y, and the two lines are at right angles. What has happened is this: When calculating Y from x, it has been assumed that the value of x is beyond argument, so all error, from whatever cause, has been ascribed to the values of y. Similarly, when calculating X from y, all errors have been regarded as affecting x, the values of y being given. However, in determining the true functional relationship between x and y neither of these extreme situations is likely to obtain. Admittedly it is not in general possible to decide which variate has caused the scatter of the points from a line, but it is reasonable to assume that neither is perfect. (Imprecision of measurement alone would make perfection impossible.) Consequently, the line representing the true natural relationship must be assumed to be somewhere between the two regression lines, the exact position depending on the extent to which one variate or the other is more subject to error. When the regression lines are at right angles, that is, $r = 0$, the true relationship, if one exists, is completely submerged by error, and one estimate of it is as good as another.

It should be emphasized that the "true relationship" referred to could be an amalgam of two conflicting relationships of the kind considered previously. With regression coefficients, as with correlation coefficients, it is possible for the value to depend on the cause of the differences; if one stimulus is more important, the sign will be positive, but it will be negative if a different stimulus predominates. Consequently an investigator is ill-advised if he works out regression coefficients and tries to build a vast theoretical structure upon them. The function of regression is to provide a means of estimating the value of one thing from the value of another; a regression coefficient justly takes into account extraneous variation irrelevant to the relationship and strikes a balance between the effects of various stimuli. Such a quantity can be invaluable for purposes of estimation, but it does not provide the material out of which scientific laws are fashioned.

10.6 THE ACCURACY OF ESTIMATION OF REGRESSION LINES

Given two variates, a regression line $Y = a + bx$ has been found, where

$$b = \frac{C_{xy}}{C_{xx}}$$

and $\quad a = \bar{y} - b\bar{x}$

This provides an estimate of Y, and the question arises as to how good it is. This comes down to asking how well a and b have been estimated.

The standard error of b is E/C_{xx}, where E is the error mean squared deviation for y after adjustment by x. It is known that the sum of squared deviations is $C_{yy}(1 - r^2)$ or $C_{yy} - C_{xy}^2/C_{xx}$, and that this has one degree of freedom fewer than C_{yy} has. Accordingly E is readily found.

The denominator in the expression for the standard error of b is C_{xx}, and this leads to an important result. The greater the variation in x, the greater C_{xx} will be, and the better estimated b will be. Therefore, if a good estimate of b, and hence of Y, is desired, as big a range as possible must be sought in x, an obvious precaution that is sometimes neglected.

For any value of x, the corresponding value of Y is estimated with a standard error of

$$\sqrt{\frac{E}{f}\left[\frac{1}{n} + \frac{(x - \bar{x})^2}{C_{xx}}\right]}$$

where f is the number of degrees of freedom for E and n is the number of data that have gone to the estimation of $\bar{y}$. Thus, in the example of the trees, if those on their own roots have x equal to 1.500, then it is to be expected that y will equal $-0.978 + 1.940(1.500) = 1.932$, the standard error of this estimate being

$$\sqrt{\frac{1}{31}\,(0.052\ 150)\left[\frac{1}{9}+\frac{(0.107)^2}{0.041\ 482}\right]} = 0.0255$$

If, however, the value of Y to be estimated is that corresponding to $x = \bar{x} = 1.607$, the second term in the parentheses will equal zero, and the standard error will be only 0.0137. Either figure is low and shows the value of Y to have been well estimated. If the standard error is multiplied by t, confidence limits can be set as for any other quantity. Taking $P = 0.05$ and 31 degrees of freedom, it appears that t equals 2.039; hence for $x = 1.500$, y lies between $1.932 \pm (2.039)(0.0255)$, i.e., 1.880 and 1.984. Also, if two treatments have adjusted treatment means of x that differ by D, and if one treatment has m plots and the other n, then the standard error of their difference in Y is

$$\sqrt{\frac{E}{f}\left[\frac{1}{m}+\frac{1}{n}+\frac{D^2}{C_{xx}}\right]}$$

10.7   THE COMPARISON OF REGRESSION COEFFICIENTS

In the example given it has been assumed that the regression line of y on x is the same for all rootstocks. Experience with studies of this kind makes such an assumption very reasonable; nevertheless it might be well to examine it, because similar data could arise in situations where such an assumption is by no means reasonable. Thus, pharmacologists are often concerned to relate y, some characteristic affected by a drug, and x, the dose given. With many preparations it might seem reasonable to assume that men and women would react in much the same way. The experimenter could then proceed as was done with the data of trunk circumference, i.e., working out C_{xx}, C_{xy}, and C_{yy} within sexes so as to eliminate any differences between men and women in the general level of x and y, but evaluating b, the regression coefficient, as if it were the same for both sexes. If, however, it were a question of injecting a sex hormone, such an assumption could be absurd; there are a number of intermediate cases where the assumption should be examined. It will therefore be examined for the plum data by way of illustration.

If trees on their own roots are considered in isolation, $C_{yy} - C_{xy}^2/C_{xx}$ equals 0.014 019 with 7 degrees of freedom. The corresponding figure for trees on Common Plum is 0.008 953, for those on Common Mussel,

0.019 998, and on Myrobalan B, 0.007 043. In fact, if separate regression coefficients are fitted in each group, the total sum of squares attributable to error is 0.050 013 with 28 degrees of freedom.

The stage has now been reached when the general method for dealing with nonorthogonal data can be applied. The method is to work out two sums of squares, one on the assumption that the differences under study can be ignored, and the other that they should be allowed for. The differences here are those between the regression coefficients for the various rootstocks. If they are really the same, it is reasonable to estimate the common value by pooling sums of squares and products from all rootstocks. Then $C_{xx} = 0.041\ 482$, $C_{xy} = 0.080\ 471$, and $C_{yy} = 0.208\ 256$, so $C_{yy} - C_{xy}^2/C_{xx}$ equals 0.052 150 with 31 degrees of freedom, a result that has already been obtained. This, together with the result in the preceding paragraph, leads to the analysis of variance in Table 10.5. The value of F is far from significant, so there is no evidence that the regression coefficients are different for different rootstocks.

Table 10.5
Analysis of variance to test significance of the differences between regression coefficients

Source	df	Sum of squares
Between regression coefficients	3	0.002 137
Error	28	0.050 013
Total	31	0.052 150

10.8 PARTIAL REGRESSION

If there are three variates, the question may well arise how far one of them, the dependent variate, y, can be estimated from the other two, w and x, the independent variates. At first sight there is no difficulty; a unit change in x will induce a change in y equal to C_{xy}/C_{xx}, while a unit change in w will induce a change in y of C_{wy}/C_{ww}. By an extension of what has been said, if w equals $\bar{w}$, and x equals $\bar{x}$, then Y will equal $\bar{y}$. By use of the two regression coefficients just cited, values of Y can be found for other values of w and x.

The argument has, however, left out of account the fact that w and x are perhaps related. Therefore, if w changes, it will have its direct effect on Y, but it will also change x and thus have a further indirect effect on Y.

Accordingly, if the separate effects of w and x are added, no account being taken of indirect effects, a wrong result will be obtained. "Partial regression coefficients" are needed, analogous to partial correlation coefficients, and in which only direct effects are taken into account.

The partial regression coefficient of y on w, effects of x being eliminated, is written $_yb_{w \cdot x}$ and equals

$$\frac{C_{wy}C_{xx} - C_{wx}C_{xy}}{C_{ww}C_{xx} - C_{wx}{}^2}$$

It will be seen that if w and x are uncorrelated (i.e., $C_{wx} = 0$),

$$_yb_{w \cdot x} = C_{wy}/C_{ww} = {}_yb_w$$

the ordinary regression coefficient of y on w, as would be expected. Also, $_yb_{x \cdot w}$ equals

$$\frac{C_{ww}C_{xy} - C_{wx}C_{wy}}{C_{ww}C_{xx} - C_{wx}{}^2}$$

By an extension of the case with only one independent variate, where there are two, Y equals

$$(\bar{y} - {}_yb_{x \cdot w}\bar{x} - {}_yb_{w \cdot x}\bar{w}) + {}_yb_{x \cdot w}x + {}_yb_{w \cdot x}w$$

Also, for one independent variate, x, that part of the sum of squared deviations of y that could be accounted for by the regression on x is $C_{xy}{}^2/C_{xx}$. This could be written $_yb_xC_{xy}$. By an extension to two independent variates, the part that could be accounted for by regression on both w and x is $_yb_{w \cdot x}C_{wy} + {}_yb_{x \cdot w}C_{xy}$ with 2 degrees of freedom.

In the example, $_yb_{w \cdot x} = +1.473\,464$, and $_yb_{x \cdot w} = +0.678\,354$, so the value of the sum of squares attributable to the regressions is $0.171\,282$. This equals the value ascribed to correlations. Ordinarily the partial regression coefficients are not worked out to so many decimal places, though a good number are needed if the sum of squared deviations is required.

10.9   CURVILINEAR REGRESSION

Partial regression methods have an important use when it is suspected that two variates, x and y, are related by a curve. One way is to estimate y from x and w, where for each plot, w is equal to x^2. In effect, the relationship fitted is

$$Y = a + bx + cx^2$$

Of course, there should be no suggestion that this neat algebraic curve really represents a biological law. As has been said, at their best, regression coefficients are only a means of estimation, but a straight line does at least represent a conceivable relationship, whereas no one is likely to believe in a parabola. However, for many purposes a good fit can be obtained; often it will be much better than that given by a straight line.

Further, this approach provides a test of straightness of the regression relationship because, if $c = 0$, the line will be straight. Accordingly, an error sum of squared deviations can be found representing the variation in y after allowing for both x and x^2. It will have 2 degrees of freedom fewer than those for C_{yy} alone. The calculation can now be repeated allowing only for x, and a new error sum of squared deviations found with 1 degree of freedom fewer than for C_{yy}. The difference between these two values with 1 degree of freedom represents the sum of squared deviations due to c, i.e., it provides a test for the curvilinear element in the relationship.

Often a better fit is given by the relationship

$$Y = a + bx + c\sqrt{x}$$

Again, it is easy to try fitting with x alone to judge the importance of c.

CHAPTER ELEVEN

THE ANALYSIS
OF COVARIANCE

ONCE METHODS ARE AVAILABLE FOR
DISCERNING HOW ONE QUANTITY AFFECTS
ANOTHER, IT BECOMES POSSIBLE TO REMOVE
THE EFFECTS OF CERTAIN SOURCES OF
VARIATION IRRELEVANT TO THE EXPERIMENT.

In the study of regression presented in the last chapter one important question was left unasked. Not only is the question of importance on its own account, but it leads to one of the most useful of statistical techniques. The question is this: Do the rootstocks differ in respect to y, allowance having been made for their differences in respect to x? The technique is that of the analysis of covariance.

11.1   THE NEED TO ADJUST ONE VARIATE BY ANOTHER

The question is one of evident relevance in many contexts. Thus, with the data considered in the last two chapters it might be of interest to know whether the rootstocks affected habit or not. Within a group of trees on the same stock, it is clear that those with thicker trunks weigh more, but it could well be that on some rootstocks the trees are heavier relative to their trunk sizes.

To take another example, an experimenter measures the final weights of a number of animals, but he would like to eliminate the residual effects of their weights at the beginning of the experiment, this being clearly a possible source of error. In another investigation, plants have been grown in a greenhouse, and blocks have been formed on the basis of the distance from the glass. However, it appears later that the position along the greenhouse is also of importance, and it is desired to allow for this although the design took no account of it. There are many instances when it becomes desirable to allow for differences that cannot or have not been considered in evolving the blocking system.

It should not be thought that these adjustments are needed only to remedy defects in the design. It is quite true that the animal experiment could have had its blocks formed on the basis of initial weight, but this might have prevented blocking on some better basis, e.g., parentage. Also, if blocks had been formed so as to minimize the effect of initial weight, it is most unlikely that they could have been formed so that each was initially uniform in that respect. In any case, the experimenter might have doubts about how important initial weight was going to be and would therefore welcome a method by which he could allow for it if it appeared to matter but could ignore it if not. Further, there might be half a dozen other variates of equal status, and it would be quite impossible to form blocks taking all of them into account.

A lot will depend upon the expected correlation coefficient between the variate under study and the one whose effect is to be eliminated. If r exceeds $+0.8$ or is less than -0.8, it is evident that there can be no major source of variation in y to compare with the effect of x, and there would be little reason for seeking an alternative to blocking on the basis of x.

An alternative simplification would be to avoid adjustments by carrying out an analysis of variance on $(y - x)$ or some such variate. This is indeed a possibility, but it throws away a valuable facility. Probably animals that are heavier than average at the start will be heavier at the end, but the law relating the two weights may be complex; a simple difference is unlikely to be enough. The method of covariance evaluates b, the regression relationship, afresh for each body of data; this provides a useful degree of flexibility.

In general, questions that concern covariance as an alternative to blocking and as an alternative to an assumed function should be decided in favor of covariance. However, caution is needed because the method of covariance itself implies a number of assumptions, and these may not be justified. These will be considered later.

11.2   COMPUTATIONS IN THE ANALYSIS OF COVARIANCE

To return to the data on girths and weights of plum trees, it is not difficult to compare the mean values of y after allowance for x. Thus for trees on their own roots the mean of x is 1.607, which is not far from the general mean of 1.609, the difference being only -0.002. Since the regression coefficient is 1.940, the mean value of y would be different by $-0.004 (=0.002 \times 1.940)$, i.e., it would be 2.152 instead of 2.148 if the trees on their own roots had average girths. By a similar argument those on Common Plum would have a mean value of y equal to 2.210; those on Common Mussel, 2.163; and those on Myrobalan B, 2.158. These differences are due to habit, the effect of the differing trunk girths having been eliminated by the adjustments.

Comparison of these adjusted values in pairs is easy because the formula for the standard error of a difference was given in the last chapter, so a t test is possible. (If it is desired to quote the standard error for an unspecified difference, a difficulty arises. The difference for a pair of treatments has its own standard error according to the extent to which the treatments differ in x, that is, according to the value of D. It is usually best to quote the largest and smallest standard errors, making it clear that all others lie between them.) It is also possible to carry out an F test. First, a complete analysis of variance is carried out for both x^2 and y^2, and an analysis of covariance for xy. Here there is a one-way classification, and the analyses are given in Table 11.1.

Table 11.1
Analyses of variance and covariance for the data in Table 10.3

Source	df	x^2	xy	y^2
Treatments	3	0.189 642	0.398 561	0.842 209
Error	32	0.041 482	0.080 471	0.208 256
Total	35	0.231 124	0.479 032	1.050 465

The error sum of squared deviations for y adjusted by x has the familiar form $[0.208\ 256 - (0.080\ 471)^2/0.041\ 482]$ or $0.052\ 150$, with 31 degrees of freedom. Merging treatments into error, following the usual practice with nonorthogonal data, gives a sum of squared deviations for error and treatments combined of $[1.050\ 465 - (0.479\ 032)^2/0.231\ 124]$ or $0.057\ 614$, with 34 degrees of freedom. Accordingly, the analysis of variance for y adjusted by x is that in Table 11.2.

Clearly there is little evidence that the different rootstocks have led to different tree weights in relation to trunk circumferences, i.e., a large tree on a dwarfing rootstock has the same shape as a small tree on a vigorous one, at least as far as this particular relationship is concerned.

When two treatment means have both been adjusted to the same value

Table 11.2
Adjusted analysis of variance for y for the data in Table 10.3

Source	df	Sum of squares	Mean square	F
Treatments	3	0.005 464	0.001 821	1.08
Error	31	0.052 150	0.001 682	
Total	34	0.057 614		

of x, where before they differed in x by an amount D, the standard error of the difference between them is

$$\sqrt{\left[\frac{1}{m} + \frac{1}{n} + \frac{D^2}{C_{xx}}\right] \text{error mean square}}$$

where m and n are the numbers of observations for the two treatments. This expression has already been given in Section 10.6.

Although more work is needed to adjust by two variates, the operation is quite practicable if it is called for. The expressions for the two partial regression coefficients have already been given in Section 10.4. If it is necessary to adjust w by an amount d_w, and x by d_x, the adjustment required in y equals

$$_yb_{w.x}d_w + _yb_{x.w}d_x$$

Further, if two treatments differ by D_w in respect to w, and by D_x in respect to x, and if both means of y are adjusted to common values for both these variates, the standard error of their difference is

$$\sqrt{\left[\frac{1}{m} + \frac{1}{n} + \frac{D_w^2 C_{xx} - 2D_w D_x C_{wx} + D_x^2 C_{ww}}{C_{ww}C_{xx} - C_{wx}^2}\right] \text{error mean square}}$$

These computations are not made much more difficult by the design being nonorthogonal if it is one of those described in Chapter 6. The first task is to work out S', the error sum of squares when treatments are included in error. Often this is obtained as a function of summation terms, and these may be calculated for the product xy with little more difficulty than for the squares x^2 and y^2. Then the treatment sum of squares is worked out, the first step being to add the squares of the values of Q; for the analysis of covariance one multiplies the values of Q for the two variates, and so on. In fact, the analysis of covariance is found easily enough. Once found, the adjusted analysis of variance for y can be found from it, as well as the two unadjusted analyses of variance, in the same way that Table 11.2 was found from Table 11.1.

Treatment means of y have to be adjusted twice, once for the non-orthogonality of the design and again for the effect of x. First, means are worked out for each variate; for a given treatment these may be called m_x and m_y, it being understood that each has been adjusted for the design as in the analysis of variance. Then the general mean, $\bar{m}$, is subtracted from each value of m_x to give $(m_x - \bar{m})$. This is multiplied by b and subtracted from m_y to give

$$m_y - b(m_x - \bar{m})$$

which is therefore the mean of y after both adjustments have been made.

Standard errors are found as for the orthogonal case except that m and n must be taken as the numbers of effective replicates, not actual.

11.3   USES OF THE ANALYSIS OF COVARIANCE

Usually the analysis of covariance is employed only when the independent variate, x, is unaffected by the treatments. In the example given here this condition does not hold, and care is needed in interpreting the results. The analysis of covariance has acquired a bad reputation in some circles because of naive conclusions. Typical is its mistaken use in a series of barley experiments in which records were taken of x, the germination rate, and y, the yield, and it was found that the treatments did not differ in respect to yield, though this conclusion was obviously absurd. What happened was this: much of the error of the experiment had arisen from differential germination, so an analysis of covariance was used, y being adjusted by x. This indeed succeeded in reducing the error mean squared deviation, but it also eliminated the mechanism whereby the treatments affected the yield. Of course, the real interpretation is that the treatments led to different germination rates and thereby affected the yields. Such a result could have been very illuminating. In the numerical example given here, much the same conclusion has been found. On different rootstocks, trees are of different size, but there is no evidence of an effect on tree weight that is not paralleled by an effect on trunk girth. If the experimenter wanted to know merely if there were effects on tree weight, he should have confined himself to an analysis of variance for y, even though he might recognize that much of the variation in y was related to variation in x.

Usually, however, the variate x is measured before the experiment begins. There need then be no fear that the analysis of variance will eliminate part of the effects of treatments. Sometimes the use of x will alter the relative values of the means of y, but this can be nothing but gain. It means that an unlucky randomization has allocated an unfairly large number of good plots to some treatments and an unfairly small number to others and that this misfortune has been remedied.

One useful application of the analysis of covariance is with missing plots. The unknown value is filled in with any number that comes into the experimenter's head—it does not matter what, though it saves trouble if he thinks of something easy like zero. Then the variate x is written down; it equals 1 for the missing plot and 0 for the others. Finally, an analysis of variance is carried out in which y, the variate under study, is adjusted by x. For purposes of evaluating treatment means, the mean of the defective treatment is adjusted to $x = 0$, like the rest. (It might appear at first sight that all treatments should be adjusted to make x equal to its general mean, but this would be a mistake.) One advantage of this method is the automatic provision for the adjustment for nonorthogonality; another is its availability for any design, orthogonal or nonorthogonal. If two plots are missing, two independent variates are needed, and so on.

Sometimes two plots become mixed, i.e., a figure can be given for the total of their yields but no one is certain how much came from each plot. The procedure here is to assign values to the two plots, subject only to the condition that their sum must be the known total of the plots. Again trouble can be saved—in this instance by assigning the figure of the total to one plot and 0 to the other. Then x is formed equal to $+1$ for one of the mixed plots, -1 for the other, and 0 for the rest of the plots. Covariance will give a correct analysis. If three plots become mixed, two independent variates are needed. For one of the plots, w and x both equal $+1$; for another, w equals $+1$ and x equals -1; for the third, w equals -2 and x equals 0. For the remaining plots, w and x both equal 0. Arbitrary values are assigned to the plots, adding up to the correct total.

There is another way in which covariance can be used as an alternative to blocks, though it is usually regarded as something of a salvage device. Suppose an experiment has been designed with a system of blocks that looked reasonable at the time, but now it appears that there are effects of importance that were ignored. If these are of a kind that can be put on a metrical scale, e.g., distance along the row, covariance is often a valuable device. However, a single independent variate is not always enough. The dependent variate may indeed tend to increase as one passes further along the greenhouse, but it does not necessarily do so linearly. A second variate, w, equal to x^2 or $\sqrt{x}$ can often be useful.

Sometimes too an experiment is conducted on material that later proves to have been mixed. For example, with some species of test animal it is not possible to determine sex before starting an experiment on newly born specimens. Subsequently it will appear that some are male and some female. If a variate x is formed, equal to 0 for each male and 1 for each female, there should be no difficulty in using it as the independent variate in the analysis of covariance. A question that sometimes arises concerns the standard value of x to which all treatment means should be adjusted, but this must depend upon the wishes of the experimenter; there is no statistical rule. If he adjusts all x to 0, he is evaluating y for a population of males; if to 1, for a population of females; if to $\frac{1}{2}$, for a population in which the sexes were equally represented; if to the general mean of the experiment, for a population with the balance of sexes actually found in the experimental material; and so on. (It does not matter to treatment differences which standard value of x is adopted, only to actual treatment means.) The same approach can be used where it belatedly appears that the material was mixed in some other way, possibly as the result of a mistake. If there are three classes, they can be allowed for by two independent variates, w being made equal respectively to $+1$, -1, and 0 for the three classes, and x to $+1$, $+1$, and -2.

11.4   ASSUMPTIONS IN THE ANALYSIS OF COVARIANCE

The example just given, in which allowance is made for sex differences not apparent at the initiation of the experiment, obviously involves an assumption, namely, that the effect of the treatments on y is the same for both sexes. Possibly the assumption is justified, but the experimenter should recognize what is happening and bring his biological judgment to bear; otherwise a statistical collaborator may go ahead and produce a nonsensical result.

The assumption can be expressed more generally by saying that b must be the same for all treatments, i.e., a change in x, sex or whatever it may be, must always have the same effect on y. For a one-way classification this is tested easily enough; indeed, the method has been given in Section 10.7. For more complicated designs a test may need more ingenuity. Nevertheless, the assumption is implicit in all uses of covariance, whether it can be tested or not, and it is a biological one. It may be obviously justified or obviously absurd; it is for a biologist to accept it or reject it, not a statistician.

Also implicit is the assumption of homogeneity of error in respect to y after adjustment by x. With a one-way classification, Bartlett's test is as feasible as when there is only one variate, though more complicated designs make testing difficult. Whether the assumption can be tested or not, it is always being made, and the experimenter should consider it. (No mention has been made of homogeneity of error of x because no assumptions concerning it are implied.)

It is sometimes said that the analysis of covariance implies the assumption that the residuals of x and the residues of y are related linearly. It would be better to say that the analysis is carried out as if they were; it is not made invalid by their being related in some other way, though it may be rendered less effective thereby.

Also, in the analysis of covariance, as in the analysis of variance, a lot depends upon the choice of suitable transformations. Indeed, the method of measurement becomes more important because there are more assumptions to be justified. Thus, y may have to be transformed, as in the analysis of variance, to secure homogeneity of error and additivity, but at the same time it is important not to destroy the relationship with x. This may also be transformed, not because homogeneity of error and additivity of the independent variable matter, but in order to secure a closer relationship with y or its transformed values and to make the relationship as close as possible to a straight line. Also, the value of b should still be the same for each treatment. Instances occur, however, in which all ends cannot be attained simultaneously; it is then usually of first importance to obtain the best characteristics for y, the dependent variate.

Residuals in the analysis of covariance are found easily enough. First they are found for x and y separately and are, say, R_x and R_y respectively. Then the residual in the analysis of covariance is $R_y - bR_x$. It follows from this that if plots are missing, it is sufficient to fit missing values for each variate separately and then to proceed. Since $R_x = 0 = R_y$, the residual in the analysis of covariance will also be 0.

CHAPTER TWELVE

MULTIVARIATE METHODS

A DESCRIPTION OF COMPONENT ANALYSIS, WHICH IS USEFUL FOR SUGGESTING HOW A NUMBER OF OBSERVED QUANTITIES ARE BEING AFFECTED BY A SMALLER NUMBER OF UNDERLYING STIMULI.

The methods described in Chapters 10 and 11 involve the simultaneous use of several variates, but most of them are not truly "multivariate" because one of the variates has a special position and the others are introduced only for the light they can shed on its variation, or in order to provide an estimate of it. In this chapter methods will be examined in which all variates have equal status. Most are essentially component analysis or one of its derivatives.

12.1   THE RESOLUTION OF CONFLICTING CORRELATIONS

In Chapter 10 it was pointed out that two variates can be imperfectly correlated because in reality they are associated in two or more ways that conflict; this means that an increase in one leads to a change in the other which will be large or small, positive or negative, according to the cause behind the change. The position is not altered if their association depends upon common causation; it is still possible for the form of association between them to vary according to the nature of the stimulus that is affecting the organism upon which they are measured.

For many purposes this does not matter. In adjusting data by covariance, for example, a regression coefficient is worked out for each body of data and may vary a great deal from one experiment to another. If the error is sometimes the result of stimuli that lead to a positive correlation between the independent and dependent variates, and sometimes of stimuli that lead to a negative correlation, the regression coefficient will be positive or negative according to circumstances. Usually both kinds of stimuli will operate, and the coefficient will take up an intermediate value, giving due weight to each stimulus according to the magnitude of its action on the organism. These remarks apply not only to the analysis of covariance, but to the use of regression coefficients in general; they are calculated from the data and are correct for those data, but they do not necessarily apply in other circumstances. They do not, in fact, represent laws of nature.

This brings up the question of whether it is possible to look behind correlation coefficients to discern the mechanisms, possibly conflicting ones, that bring them about. The strict reply must be that a definite answer is not feasible, because there is another way in which imperfect correlations arise, namely, from a single relationship between the two variates being obscured by poor measurement or the intervention of chance effects. It is never possible to decide certainly whether this is the case or whether there are conflicting relationships.

Nevertheless methods exist that will suggest mechanisms whereby the observed correlations could have come about. To do this is to venture into fresh fields that statisticians often find very strange, because they are not being asked to test a hypothesis or to estimate a quantity in a hypothesis, but are being required to help formulate the hypothesis in the first place. They do not always appreciate what these methods are for, and they sometimes assert that the whole operation is useless because no standard errors are ever assigned to quantities and no significance levels are ever evaluated. Nevertheless, research begins with the formulation of a hypothesis, and statisticians should be glad to find themselves thus involved at the start.

An opposite difficulty exists for biologists, who often expect too much from multivariate methods. They see a hypothesis that has been evolved by an "objective method" and suppose that it must be superior to one they thought up for themselves, but this is not necessarily so. Objective methods are no better than their own conceptual bases; if these are mistaken, the results are wrong. (For example, to consider for a moment a very different problem, statistical techniques exist for effecting classification. If an electronic computer were supplied with the characters used by Linnaeus to divide a certain family into genera and species, it might well produce the Linnaean classification, but this would not prove that Linnaeus was "right"; it would prove only that he had the qualities of a conscientious clerk. His skill lay in selecting the characters on which the classification should be based, and this lies quite outside anything done by the computer.) The hypotheses evolved by multivariate methods are like any other and should be accepted only if they can be coordinated with other knowledge and can be confirmed by experimental evidence.

As a matter of fact these methods are not as objective as they appear to be; everyone seems to have his own variant, and sometimes hot disputes arise as to which is best. Where hypotheses are being sought it is not to be supposed that a single approach will be best in all circumstances. The only test of correctness is success, i.e., the hypothesis suggested proves to be a useful one.

Before proceeding further, it may be helpful to examine more closely the nature of the correlation coefficient itself. So far it has been defined as

$$\frac{C_{xy}}{\sqrt{C_{xx}C_{yy}}}$$

If C_{xx}, C_{xy}, and C_{yy} are all divided by the degrees of freedom, which are the same for each, to produce M_{xx}, M_{xy}, and M_{yy}, the correlation coefficient can be written

$$\frac{M_{xy}}{\sqrt{M_{xx}M_{yy}}}$$

This expression can arise in another way. The covariance of x and y is M_{xy}. If x is measured on a new scale in terms of its own standard deviation, $\sqrt{M_{xx}}$, as the unit, all its values are divided by this amount and the covariance becomes

$$\frac{M_{xy}}{\sqrt{M_{xx}}}$$

If y is also measured in terms of its standard deviation, $\sqrt{M_{yy}}$, the covariance becomes

$$\frac{M_{xy}}{\sqrt{M_{xx}M_{yy}}}$$

which is of course r. In fact, a correlation coefficient between two variates may be thought of as their covariance after each has been expressed in terms of its own standard deviation. This approach will be found useful later.

12.2   A SIMPLE EXAMPLE OF COMPONENT ANALYSIS

Component analysis depends upon a simple mathematical theorem, which is more simply illustrated than described. The results for the study of the two girth measurements and the weight of plum trees (Table 10.3) will be very suitable. Write the sums of squares and products as a matrix, i.e., in a rectangular table with a row and a column for each variate. These are

$$\begin{pmatrix} 0.037\,398 & 0.035\,516 & 0.079\,197 \\ 0.035\,516 & 0.041\,482 & 0.080\,471 \\ 0.079\,197 & 0.080\,471 & 0.208\,256 \end{pmatrix}$$

Suppose now that some stimulus operates such that when it alters w by an amount a, it alters x by b, and y by c. Then the theorem asserts that the quantities

$$A = 0.037\ 398a + 0.035\ 516b + 0.079\ 197c$$
$$B = 0.035\ 516a + 0.041\ 482b + 0.080\ 471c$$
and $$C = 0.079\ 197a + 0.080\ 471b + 0.208\ 256c$$

will be in the ratio $a:b:c$. The coefficients are derived from the matrix.

It is now possible to estimate a, b, and c by iteration, i.e., by guessing their values and calculating a better approximation from the guesses. Thus, here it is reasonable to guess that whenever w is increased by 1, x will be increased by a like amount, and y by about 2.5, because a general effect of growth must exist, and these are the relative values of the standard deviations. Expressing these in terms of the largest, the "vector of the stimulus's action," as it will be called, is

$$\{0.4, \quad 0.4, \quad 1\}$$

Taking these as values of a, b, and c, the values of A, B, and C are

$$0.037\ 398(0.4) + 0.035\ 516(0.4) + 0.079\ 197(1.0) = 0.1084$$
$$0.035\ 516(0.4) + 0.041\ 482(0.4) + 0.080\ 471(1.0) = 0.1113$$
$$0.079\ 179(0.4) + 0.080\ 471(0.4) + 0.208\ 256(1.0) = 0.2721$$

It will be seen that four significant places have been considered sufficient. Scaling all three in terms of the largest (0.2721) gives a better approximation to the vector, namely,

$$\{0.398, \quad 0.409, \quad 1\}$$

This in turn may be used to obtain a better approximation:

$$0.037\ 398(0.398) + 0.035\ 516(0.409) + 0.079\ 197(1.000) = 0.1086$$
$$0.035\ 516(0.398) + 0.041\ 482(0.409) + 0.080\ 471(1.000) = 0.1116$$
$$0.079\ 179(0.398) + 0.080\ 471(0.409) + 0.208\ 256(1.000) = 0.2727$$

which gives the same as before, namely,

$$\{0.398, \quad 0.409, \quad 1\}$$

Hence a solution has been found. It confirms that there are general size differences, and it assigns values to the relative growth rates of the various parts. It shows also that a variance of 0.2727, corresponding to the variate by which the others are scaled, can be accounted for by general size differences. This is a large part of the total of

$$0.2871 (= 0.037\ 398 + 0.041\ 482 + 0.208\ 256)$$

so it does not appear that these data need be examined for any further effects.

It might be thought that all this is a laborious way of showing that trees differ in size, but it has done more than that. It has given relative growth rates, and it has shown that there are no further important relationships to be derived from these data, for example, no shape differences apart from those resulting from differential growth rates.

The method was here applied to the dispersion matrix, i.e., the sums of squares and products. The same result would have been obtained from the variance-covariance matrix, i.e., that obtained by dividing all values in the dispersion matrix by the degrees of freedom. Some might prefer to divide each variate by its standard deviation, i.e., to use the correlation matrix; this would have the effect of giving all variates equal weight. There is no finality about a question of this sort; the answer must be partly a matter of biological insight and partly of trying all possibilities. In an exploratory method such indefiniteness is an advantage, giving as it does flexibility, rather than a weakness.

12.3   A GEOMETRIC INTERPRETATION

With only three variates it would be quite possible to build a solid diagram with the axes of w and x at right angles on the base and the values of y measured vertically upward. Then each tree could be represented by a ball on a piece of stiff wire. First the value of w would be measured along the w axis, then the value of x at right angles to the w axis (parallel, that is to say, to the x axis), and a hole bored in the base at this point. Finally a piece of wire would be cut, its length being equal to the value of y. One end would be pushed into the hole in the base and the other into the ball. In this way a three-dimensional figure could be built up showing how the trees were distributed in terms of the three variates.

There is, however, no need to do all this, because the component analysis has shown clearly what the result would be. There is only one vector, and it is approximately that one originally guessed, namely, $\{0.4,\quad 0.4,\quad 1\}$. Hence the balls for two trees on the same rootstock would be disposed so that their difference in ω would equal their difference in x, and both would be 0.4 of their difference in y. In fact, all the balls for a rootstock would lie in a straight line.

This leads to the "standardized" form for writing a vector. Hitherto it has been written in terms of the difference in the variate most affected; it is often better to write it in terms of the difference along the line of action. This is

$$\sqrt{0.4^2 + 0.4^2 + 1.0^2} = 1.149$$

i.e., if w and x were both to change by 0.4, and y by 1.0, the two balls would be 1.149 apart. Dividing by this quantity, the vector becomes

$$\{0.348, \quad 0.348, \quad 0.870\}$$

If w and x both change by 0.348, and y changes by 0.870, the balls will be a unit distance apart, i.e., there will be unit action of the stimulus along the vector. This means that the line of action of the stimulus is disposed to the axes so that the angles it forms with them have cosines of 0.348, 0.348, and 0.870, respectively. Therefore, when a vector is expressed in standardized form, the values that make it up are called "direction cosines."

It is now possible to see uses for the vector that were not apparent before. For example, the first tree in Table 10.3 had values for w, x, and y, of 1.690, 1.663, and 2.318, respectively, whereas the rootstock means were 1.639, 1.607, and 2.148, giving deviations of +0.051, +0.056, and +0.170 for the three variates. Its deviation on the line representing the vector will therefore be

$$(0.348)(0.051) + (0.348)(0.056) + (0.870)(0.170)$$

or +0.185. This provides a measure of the effect of the stimulus on the tree in question. It might be thought that the distance should be

$$\sqrt{0.051^2 + 0.056^2 + 0.170^2}$$

or 0.186, but this is the distance between the points measured directly; what is wanted is the component in the direction of the vector, unobscured by random errors or possible other vectors. Deviations along the vector can be correlated with other quantities or examined by the analysis of variance because they measure a definable quantity, namely, the extent of action of the stimulus represented by the vector.

Also, if one vector is expected and another is found, the angle between them is easily found. Thus, someone may argue that a tree is a solid figure and the vector

$$\{1, \quad 1, \quad 3\}$$

is to be expected. After standardization this becomes

{0.302, 0.302, 0.905}

The angle it forms with

{0.348, 0.348, 0.870}

has a cosine of

(0.302)(0.348) + (0.302)(0.348) + (0.905)(0.870)

or 0.9975. In fact, it is about 1°17′ and the divergence of the two vectors is negligible.

12.4   A MORE COMPLICATED EXAMPLE OF COMPONENT ANALYSIS

Another example is an investigation conducted into the growth of apple trees. Essentially growth must depend upon the activity of meristematic tissue, which activity is of two kinds, cambial and apical. Records were made at four years from planting and at fifteen, when the trees were cut up for measurement. There was a range of rootstocks; only variation within them was measured.

Four variates were used:

e, log (trunk circumference after four years)
x, log (extension growth in the first four years)
g, log (trunk circumference after fifteen years)
w, log (weight of tree above ground after fifteen years)

It will be seen that e and g result only from cambial activity, whereas x results only from apical, and w from both. Further, e and x were measured at one time, and g and w at another. The correlation matrix was

$$\begin{pmatrix} 1.000 & 0.898 & 0.619 & 0.517 \\ 0.898 & 1.000 & 0.694 & 0.596 \\ 0.619 & 0.694 & 1.000 & 0.951 \\ 0.517 & 0.596 & 0.951 & 1.000 \end{pmatrix}$$

The calculations will not be written out in full as before, but in pairs of lines, the upper in each pair giving A, B, C, and D from the last approximation of the vector, and the lower, a, b, c, and d, the new approximation derived from the line immediately above. The first guess is a very simple one, namely,

$$\{1, \quad 1, \quad 1, \quad 1\}$$

implying a tendency for some trees to be larger than others at all times, however measured. The calculation proceeds:

3.034	3.188	3.264	3.064
0.930	0.977	1.000	0.939
2.912	3.066	3.147	2.953
0.925	0.974	1.000	0.938
2.904	3.058	3.141	2.948
0.925	0.974	1.000	0.939
2.904	3.058	3.142	2.949
0.924	0.973	1.000	0.939
2.902	3.056	3.140	2.948
0.924	0.973	1.000	0.939

The same vector has now been found twice running, and the calculation can stop. Essentially it is the one that was guessed, and it accounts for a variance of 3.140. The total is 4.000, because there are four variates, each adjusted to have unit variance, so there may well be other undiscovered effects. In order to find them it is necessary to extract from the matrix that part of it due to the vector already found.

This is done by working out the direction cosines, i.e., by dividing by

$$\sqrt{0.924^2 + 0.973^2 + 1.000^2 + 0.939^2}$$

or 1.919, which gives

$$\{0.481, \quad 0.507, \quad 0.521, \quad 0.489\}$$

Now if the stimulus has unit effect, it will change w by 0.481; if it has unit variance, it will lead to a variance of 0.481^2 in w^2 and a covariance of $(0.481)(0.507)$ in wx. However, the variance of action of the stimulus is in fact 3.140, so it accounts for $3.140(0.481)^2$ or 0.726 in the variance of w^2, of $3.140(0.481)(0.507)$ or 0.766 in the covariance of wx, and so on. In full, the matrix to be extracted is

$$\begin{pmatrix} 0.726 & 0.766 & 0.787 & 0.739 \\ 0.766 & 0.807 & 0.829 & 0.778 \\ 0.787 & 0.829 & 0.852 & 0.800 \\ 0.739 & 0.778 & 0.800 & 0.751 \end{pmatrix}$$

which leaves

$$\begin{pmatrix} 0.274 & 0.132 & -0.168 & -0.222 \\ 0.132 & 0.193 & -0.135 & -0.182 \\ -0.168 & -0.135 & 0.148 & 0.151 \\ -0.222 & -0.182 & 0.151 & 0.249 \end{pmatrix}$$

The next task is to derive a vector from this residuary matrix. The first and second variates are positively related, as are the third and fourth, but other relations are negative. This implies some such vector as

$$\{1, \quad 1, \quad -1, \quad -1\}$$

or a balance between the variates measured at four years and those measured at fifteen. Accordingly this vector will be tried, with these results:

0.796	0.642	−0.602	−0.804
−0.990	−0.799	0.749	1.000
−0.725	−0.568	0.536	0.727
−0.997	−0.781	0.737	1.000
−0.722	−0.564	0.533	0.724
−0.997	−0.779	0.736	1.000
−0.722	−0.563	0.533	0.723
−0.999	−0.779	0.737	1.000
−0.722	−0.564	0.533	0.724
−0.997	−0.779	0.736	1.000

At this point the phenomenon of "oscillation" has been encountered. The vector

$$\{-0.997, \quad -0.779, \quad 0.736, \quad 1.000\}$$

leads to

$$\{-0.999, \quad -0.779, \quad 0.737, \quad 1.000\}$$

and vice versa. One reaction would be to leave the calculation at this point, on the ground that it does not matter which is correct, because they are both so similar. Since an additional variance of at least 0.723, making $3.863 (= 3.140 + 0.723)$ in all, has been accounted for, there is little reason in this instance to continue. If, however, it was desirable to extract the effect of this vector also, in order to examine the data for a third one, some better determination would be needed. The remedy is to work with an additional decimal place. Continuing therefore

$$-0.997 \quad -0.779 \quad 0.736 \quad 1.000$$

gives

$$
\begin{array}{llll}
-0.7217 & -0.5633 & 0.5326 & 0.7232 \\
-0.9979 & -0.7789 & 0.7364 & 1.0000 \\[6pt]
-0.7220 & -0.5635 & 0.5328 & 0.7235 \\
-0.9979 & -0.7789 & 0.7364 & 1.0000
\end{array}
$$

To three decimal places the vector is therefore

$$\{-0.998, \quad -0.779, \quad 0.736, \quad 1.000\}$$

which gives the effect numerical form and shows that some trees do better at fifteen years than would be expected from their performance at four. It would be possible to standardize this vector also and remove its effect in order to start a search for a third, but with so much variation already accounted for this is not needed.

12.5   THE INTERPRETATION OF COMPONENT ANALYSES

Before proceeding further, it will be well to ask what has and what has not been proved by the analysis in the last section.

It has been shown that the data could have arisen from the action of the two vectors found. It does not follow that they did; possibly there are other hypotheses that would account for them. (Perhaps no one can think of any, but that is no argument for asserting that none can exist.) Also, the apparent objectivity of the method is no reason for believing the results. For one thing, it is not objective, decisions having been called for at three points, (1) in choosing the four measurements in the first place, (2) in transforming them to logarithms, and (3) in using the correlation matrix instead of the variance-covariance matrix. Secondly, if a method is truly mechanical and calls for no decisions from its operator, it must be that the person who devised it made the decisions himself and built them into the method. Thus, here the method is that of component analysis in which all variation is assumed to result from the action of independent stimuli represented by vectors. This may be quite wrong; the low correlations may not arise because of conflicting effects, but for the reason given in the classical theory of correlation, namely, that each variate is affected independently by random variation. Consequently the analysis in itself proves very little.

Nevertheless, there are two important things in its favor. For one thing, both vectors make good biological sense. The first is not far from

$$\{\tfrac{1}{2}, \quad \tfrac{1}{2}, \quad \tfrac{1}{2}, \quad \tfrac{1}{2}\}$$

This means that in terms of its own standard deviation each variate was equally affected by some stimulus that led to increased growth by both kinds of meristem over both periods. It is not clear what this stimulus was, but the vector is no mathematical enigma; it has a clear biological meaning. The second vector approximates to

$$\{\tfrac{1}{2}, \quad \tfrac{1}{2}, \quad -\tfrac{1}{2}, \quad -\tfrac{1}{2}\}$$

and means that for some reason there are trees in which the two early measurements were larger than would be expected from the general level of all the variates, the late measurements being smaller. Again the implication is intelligible.

A second argument in favor of the analysis is that these two vectors turn up again and again. This does not prove that they have any fundamental biological meaning, but they cannot be dismissed as chance. Thus, here are the corresponding vectors found in three other apple tree experiments in which the same four variates were measured:

(1)	+0.48	+0.47	+0.55	+0.51
	+0.51	+0.55	−0.44	−0.50
(2)	+0.46	+0.50	+0.55	+0.49
	+0.55	+0.48	−0.41	−0.55
(3)	+0.50	+0.49	+0.50	+0.51
	+0.50	+0.52	−0.50	−0.49
	+0.57	−0.56	+0.41	−0.43

The last study was made on older trees, and here a third vector was found, which appears to show an imbalance between apical and cambial activity, but this is in addition to the usual two vectors. The vectors do at least fall into the category of repeatable phenomena. Also, the vectors are the same though the correlations are not. For example, in experiment (2) the correlation matrix was

$$\begin{pmatrix} 1.000 & 0.835 & 0.358 & 0.178 \\ 0.835 & 1.000 & 0.424 & 0.266 \\ 0.358 & 0.424 & 1.000 & 0.939 \\ 0.178 & 0.266 & 0.939 & 1.000 \end{pmatrix}$$

In this instance the second vector was very pronounced, accounting for 32 per cent of all the variation, so an attempt was made to trace its source, and it appeared to be related to depth of soil.

The real justification for accepting a hypothesis suggested in this way must always be that it has stood the test of experiment. A vector having been found, its value must be obtained for each plot, using the method given in Section 12.3. These values can then be correlated with other measurements or subjected to the analysis of variance to see if any explanation of the vector can be supported. If an explanation is thought of, it should be made the subject of experimental investigation; otherwise the conclusions are mere speculation. Nevertheless, the existence of these vectors, whatever the reason for them, is a fact of experience. They provide a description of phenomena, though not necessarily an explanation of them.

12.6   ALTERNATIVE SYSTEMS OF VECTORS

In the example given in the last section it appeared that if all trees were plotted in a four-dimensional space of e, x, g, and w, the points would differ only in one or both of the directions given by the vectors

$$\text{and} \quad \begin{array}{cccc} \{\frac{1}{2}, & \frac{1}{2}, & \frac{1}{2}, & \frac{1}{2}\} \\ \{\frac{1}{2}, & \frac{1}{2}, & -\frac{1}{2}, & -\frac{1}{2}\} \end{array}$$

because the action of stimuli is in one or the other of these directions. Consequently the points must lie in a two-dimensional space, i.e., a plane. Since, however, a plane can be defined by any two lines in it, this description cannot be unique. It may be asked why the component analysis picked one certain pair of vectors out of an infinitude of possibilities. The answer is that the two vectors given are the only ones that represent two stimuli with independent actions at right angles.

Since stimuli need not be independent, this explanation may give rise to further questioning. Plainly, if there are two vectors (e.g., those given), and an action of p in the first is associated with q in the other, the total effect will be

$$\{\tfrac{1}{2}p + \tfrac{1}{2}q, \quad \tfrac{1}{2}p + \tfrac{1}{2}q, \quad \tfrac{1}{2}p - \tfrac{1}{2}q, \quad \tfrac{1}{2}p - \tfrac{1}{2}q\}$$

This vector may look rather different when standardized, but it must lie in the plane defined by the original pair. It is now only necessary to choose two different values of p and q to find another line in the same plane. If p and

q are replaced by q and $-p$, the second line can be shown to be at right angles to the first, i.e.,

$$\{\tfrac{1}{2}q - \tfrac{1}{2}p, \quad \tfrac{1}{2}q - \tfrac{1}{2}p, \quad \tfrac{1}{2}q + \tfrac{1}{2}p, \quad \tfrac{1}{2}q + \tfrac{1}{2}p\}$$

For example, if $p = 1 = q$, a change in the first vector being always associated with a similar change in the second, the familiar vectors become

$$\{ \quad 1, \quad 1, \quad 0, \quad 0\}$$

i.e., $\{0.71, \quad 0.71, \quad 0, \quad 0\}$

after standardization. At this point someone may say that he already had some such vector in mind. Since apical and cambial activity appear always to be in balance, it is to be expected that e and x will always change strictly together, g and w having nothing to do with the change. The fresh vector should therefore be adopted as "simpler." If now the vector at right angles to it is found, it proves to be

$$\{0, \quad 0, \quad 1, \quad 1\}$$

or $\{0, \quad 0, \quad 0.71, \quad 0.71\}$

the corresponding one for g and w.

Which pair of vectors is really "simpler?" The statistician will prefer the first because they represent independent effects; the biologist will like the second because each vector is clearly intelligible and he finds nothing strange in the idea that they are related—indeed, he might expect some correlation between growth over four years and over fifteen. The two collaborators could get quite heated about the question. They should consider that they are both talking about the same variation in the same plane; their difference is only in how they describe it.

This argument can readily be extended to three vectors or more. Whichever vectors are found, it is always possible to ask what happens if the first acts by an amount p, the second by q, the third by r, and so on. Where there are more than two vectors, it is not so easy to derive a fresh set at right angles among themselves, though it can be done. It is useless to ask which of the sets represents the true fundamental biological concepts. If one had to choose, the choice would fall on the original set, which was independent; but if this is unsatisfactory, the choice is for the biologist to make. No one else can make it for him.

The question sometimes arises whether a given vector does or does not lie in the space swept out by the ones that have been found. Thus, some experimenter might have expected the vector

$$\{0.7, \quad -0.5, \quad -0.5, \quad 0.1\}$$

—it is not clear why he should, but the suggestion will serve for illustration —and he wants to know if it does in fact lie in the space defined by

$$\{0.5, \quad 0.5, \quad 0.5, \quad 0.5\}$$
$$\{0.5, \quad 0.5, \quad -0.5, \quad -0.5\}$$

The first step is to work out the cosine of the angle between the suggested vector and each of those given by the component analysis, i.e.,

$$(0.7 \times 0.5) + (-0.5 \times 0.5) + (-0.5 \times 0.5) + (0.1 \times 0.5) = -0.10$$
$$(0.7 \times 0.5) + (-0.5 \times 0.5) + (-0.5 \times 0.5) + (0.1 \times -0.5) = 0.30$$

The vector in the space most nearly parallel to the one suggested is

$$-0.10\{0.5, \quad 0.5, \quad 0.5, \quad 0.5\}$$
$$+0.30\{0.5, \quad 0.5, \quad -0.5, \quad -0.5\}$$

or $\quad\{0.10, \quad 0.10, \quad -0.20, \quad -0.20\}$

With standardization this becomes

$$\{0.32, \quad 0.32, \quad -0.63, \quad -0.63\}$$

Its angle with the suggested vector has a cosine of

$$(0.32 \times 0.7) + (0.32 \times -0.5) + (-0.63 \times -0.5) + (-0.63 \times 0.1)$$

which comes to 0.306, so the angle must be about 72°, and the suggested vector is steeply inclined to the plane.

12.7   FACTOR ANALYSIS

As has been said, there are two main reasons why a correlation coefficient can be small; component analysis has dealt with only one, namely, the concurrent action of vectors that lead to different, or even conflicting, relationships. The other possibility is that a variate is subject to random variation in addition to that brought about by the vectors; this has not been considered.

In factor analysis the procedure is to take the variances (i.e., the elements of the matrix on the diagonal from the top left-hand corner to the bottom right-hand one) and reduce them to their "communalities," i.e., that part of them that arises from effects common to several variates. This can be done in various ways, some little better than arbitrary and some depending on precise assumptions. A component analysis is then conducted on the matrix formed. (The covariances are not altered.)

One way of deriving the communalities when working with the correlation matrix is to work out the multiple correlation coefficient of each variate with the rest and to use the squares of these values as the communalities. There are many other ways.

Factor analysis will not be taken further here, but no account of multivariate methods would be complete without a reference to it because it has been a help in many fields of research.

12.8   SOME PRACTICAL CONSIDERATIONS

As has been said, there is no fixed path for those who venture into multivariate work. Rich rewards await those who look in the right place for results. Indeed, there are no statistical techniques that correspond more closely to biological ways of thought than this, but the rewards are not for those who seek mechanically. Decisions have to be made all the time, and they have to be made with good judgment and usually on biological grounds.

The first decision relates to the variates to be studied, and here an investigator can be in a quandary. If he leaves out a variate that ought to be in, he stands a chance of maiming an important vector and making it look arbitrary or unintelligible when, in its full form, it has a ready interpretation. If, on the other hand, he puts in a variate that adds little to the investigation, but is nevertheless correlated with the other variates, the result can be the same: he has obscured what would otherwise be clear. What he wants is a set of variates that sums up the action of a set of vectors, no further variates being needed to reveal the action of the vectors, and no further vectors being needed to explain the behavior of the variates. Such a situation is rare, but it is more likely to be found by selecting a logical set of variates than by including anything that can be measured. Also, if some of the variates appear to be involved with extraneous vectors, factor analysis may provide a way out.

The next decision relates to transformations. Many of the considerations that apply in the analysis of variance apply here too, but there is a greater emphasis on obtaining straight-line relationships, a change of a certain size in x being associated with the same change in y whatever the initial values of the variates. On the other hand, homogeneity of variation counts for much less.

Next a choice has to be made between the dispersion matrix (or the variance-covariance matrix, which will yield the same vectors) and the correlation matrix. The decision must depend on several things. If the variates have diverse scales of measurements, e.g., they are a weight, a length, and a number, it can hardly be supposed that the original units of measurement have any bearing on the problem, and the correlation matrix is probably better. On the other hand, if the scales are the same, the different variances may or may not be relevant. Thus, in the two sets of data considered in this chapter, different decisions have been made. For the plum trees the dispersion matrix was used because weight is necessarily—from the geometry of the tree—related to (trunk circumference)$^{2.6}$ or (trunk circumference)$^{2.7}$. This appears in the greater variance for log(tree weight) compared with that for log(trunk circumference). On the other hand, with the apple trees the correlation matrix was used, because comparable effects on growth were in question, and it was thought better to reduce all variates to the same variance. However, there is no finality about such decisions; perhaps both were wrong. Also, of course, the effect of using the correlation matrix is to give all variates equal weight when determining how much variation is explained by a vector. This can be a good thing; otherwise finding a vector that explains some of the variation in the most variable variate will appear as a great triumph, whereas one that explains all the variation in a group of nearly constant variates may seem to verge on triviality. Whether it is or not must depend on the problem.

This brings up the question of when to give up the search for vectors and to accept that what remains in the matrix is random variation. There are tests for this, but they are laborious. Most people would feel that they could finish when 90 to 95 per cent of the variation had been extracted. There can, however, be no absolute rule of this kind. The first vector found is usually one of general size. It is not usually of much interest because everyone knows that some specimens will be larger than others, though it can provide a size measurement better than any of the variates alone. Also, it may explain 80 per cent or more of the variation. Quite a large part of what remains may be lost if a second vector removes another 12 per cent, and its discovery brings the analysis to an end.

People may be puzzled as to what vector to guess to start the iterative procedure. If they guess badly they do not necessarily waste much effort, because the successive approximations will change rapidly until the region of the vector is attained. If the iteration goes on for a long time they are apt to blame their original guess, but a more likely explanation is the existence of a further vector of approximately equal importance. (This has some bearing on when to call off the search. A vector found with difficulty can hardly be the last.) Nevertheless, the better the original guess, the quicker an answer is found. In general, it is worth paying attention to signs in the guessed vector so as to fit the signs of the larger covariances in the matrix, e.g., if two variates appear to be highly negatively correlated in the matrix, they should be given opposite signs when guessing the vector. Also, if the variation of a variate has already been largely explained, it may well be given zero in the guessed vector.

One very important decision concerns the number of data needed if reliance is to be placed on the result of analysis. The dispersion matrix should have at least 25 degrees of freedom, and more are desirable. The question sometimes arises as to which line of the analyses of variance and covariance should be used. The answer must depend on the variation being studied. It is a most useful procedure at times to start with the error line, or perhaps (error + blocks), and to add the other lines one by one, noting when a new vector appears. Such a vector obviously represents the distinctive action of the source of variation last added. Others prefer to start with the total line and subtract other lines one by one; essentially the two approaches are the same. It should be noted that some treatments are a definition or exaggeration of sources of variation that already exist in the error, whereas others are of quite a different kind. Thus, different amounts of protein added to the diet are unlikely to add a vector if the people already vary in the protein of their basic diets. Also, it is always possible that the vector added will be associated with those already present.

However, the plum tree data provide a warning. If the variation between rootstocks is added to that within rootstocks, it is expected that the vector

$$\{0.398, \quad 0.409, \quad 1\}$$

which explains nearly the whole of the variation within rootstocks, will be found again. In fact, the total line also has only one vector. It is

$$\{0.475, \quad 0.462, \quad 1\}$$

What has happened is very simple. The variation between rootstocks is much larger than that within, so it dominates the total line. The fresh vector is in fact that of the variation between rootstocks; since this has only 3 degrees of freedom, little importance can be attached to it.

SUGGESTIONS FOR FURTHER READING

In a quotation at the head of Chapter 1 the King told the White Rabbit to go on until he came to the end and then stop. In the simple matter of who stole the tarts there was perhaps a recognizable end, but in the field of statistics there is none in sight; certainly there is no suggestion that this book has reached one. There is much more that can be read, and a list may be helpful. It was compiled by asking a number of biologists who are known to be proficient at statistics what books had proved useful to them.

There are two that have provided the inspiration for much subsequent statistical work. They are:

1. Fisher, R. A.: "Statistical Methods for Research Workers," Oliver & Boyd Ltd., Edinburgh, 1925.
2. Fisher, R. A.: "The Design of Experiments," Oliver & Boyd Ltd., Edinburgh, 1935.

Neither shows its full depth at first reading and the beginner may find them difficult, but each is well worth any effort. More immediately useful are:

3. Snedecor, G. W.: "Statistical Methods," The Collegiate Press, Menasha, Wis., 1956.
4. Goulden, C. H.: "Methods of Statistical Analysis," John Wiley & Sons, Inc., New York, 1952.
5. Paterson, D. D.: "Statistical Technique in Agricultural Research," McGraw-Hill Book Company, New York, 1939.

For those who wish to know more about experimental designs and the methods of analysis appropriate to them, mention may be made of

6. Yates, F.: "The Design and Analysis of Factorial Experiments," Technical Communication No. 35 of the Commonwealth Bureau of Soil Science, 1937. Obtainable from the Commonwealth Agricultural Bureaux, Farnham Royal, Buckinghamshire, England.
7. Cochran, W. G. and G. M. Cox: "Experimental Designs," 2nd ed., John Wiley & Sons, Inc., New York, 1957.

8. Federer, W. T.: "Experimental Design: Theory and Application," The Macmillan Company, New York, 1955.
9. Kempthorne, O.: "The Design and Analysis of Experiments," John Wiley & Sons, Inc., New York, 1952.

These are given in approximately ascending order of advancement. The account of multiple-range tests in (8) is especially complete. Mention should be made also of

10. Finney, D. J.: "Experimental Design and Its Statistical Basis," Cambridge University Press, Cambridge and New York, 1955.
11. Bailey, N. T. J.: "Statistical Methods in Biology," English Universities Press, London, 1959.
12. Finney, D. J.: "An Introduction to Statistical Science in Agriculture," 2nd ed., Oliver & Boyd Ltd., Edinburgh, 1962.
13. Cox, D. R.: "Planning of Experiments," John Wiley & Sons, Inc., New York, 1958.

These books are intended to set out principles rather than to expound technical details though a lot can be learned from them in both respects. A further book is

14. Quenouille, M. H.: "The Design and Analysis of Experiment," Charles Griffin & Company, Ltd., London, 1953.

It contains many interesting ideas.
For those concerned specifically with field experiments the following may be useful:

15. Wishart, J. and H. G. Saunders: "Principles and Practice of Field Experimentation," Technical Communication No. 18 of the Commonwealth Bureau of Plant Breeding and Genetics, 1955.*
16. Pearce, S. C.: "Field Experimentation with Fruit Trees and Other Perennial Plants," Technical Communication No. 23 of the Commonwealth Bureau of Horticulture and Plantation Crops, 1953.

The first of these is concerned with annual species, the second with perennial. Both can be obtained from the address given for (6). For foresters there is

17. Jeffers, J. N. R.: "Experimental Design and Analysis in Forest Research," Almqvist and Wiksell, Stockholm, 1960.

In the present volume little attention has been given to the classical problems of distributions, e.g., the Poisson and the Binomial. For these reference may be made to

* Previously published by the Empire Cotton Growing Corporation, 1935.

18. Anderson, R. L. and T. A. Bancroft: "Statistical Theory in Research," McGraw-Hill Book Company, New York, 1952.
19. Yule, G. U. and M. G. Kendall: "Introduction to the Theory of Statistics," 14th ed., Charles Griffin & Company, Ltd., London, 1961.

The first of these is helpful about the design of experiments and the analysis of data also.
Sampling methods for surveys are rather different from the topics discussed in the present volume. Two useful references are

20. Yates, F.: "Sampling Methods for Censuses and Surveys," Charles Griffin & Company, Ltd., London, 1949.
21. Sampford, M. R.: "An Introduction to Sampling Theory with Applications to Agriculture," Oliver & Boyd Ltd., Edinburgh, 1962.

Bioassay is another subject not treated in the present text. Mention may be made of

22. Finney, D. J.: "Probit Analysis," Cambridge University Press, Cambridge and New York, 1947.
23. Finney, D. J.: "Statistical Method in Biological Assay," Charles Griffin & Company, Ltd., London, 1952.

Regression methods are considered in more detail than here in

24. Acton, F. S.: "Analysis of Straight-line Data," John Wiley & Sons, Inc., New York, 1959.

Medical men will find much that is useful in

25. Hill, A. Bradford: "Principles of Medical Statistics," 6th ed., *The Lancet*, London, 1956.
26. Mainland, D.: "Elementary Medical Statistics," 2nd ed., W. B. Company, Philadelphia, 1963.
27. Armitage, P.: "Sequential Medical Trials," Blackwell Scientific Publications, Ltd., Oxford, 1960.

These books merit reading by workers in other fields. There is much good sense in (26), while (27) provides a useful survey of sequential methods.
Little has been said in this book of genetics, though of all biological fields it is the one most dependent on probabilistic concepts. A book that may be found useful is

28. Mather, K.: "The Measurement of Linkage in Heredity," 2nd ed., Methuen & Co., Ltd., London, 1951.

Another is

29. Mather, K.: "Biometrical Genetics: The Study of Continuous Variation," Methuen & Co., Ltd., London, 1949.

Geneticists should acquaint themselves also with the χ^2 test and the binomial theory, for which purpose (19) is recommended.
A general introduction to multivariate methods is afforded by

30. Kendall, M. G.: "A Course in Multivariate Analysis," Charles Griffin & Company, Ltd., London, 1957.

For those who would like to know something of the mathematical bases of statistical methods there is

31. Hoel, P. G.: "Introduction to Mathematical Statistics," John Wiley & Sons, Inc., New York, 1947.

A general mathematical book of interest to the biologist is

32. Smith, C. A. B.: "Biomathematics," Charles Griffin & Company, Ltd., London, 1953.

APPENDIX I

CRITICAL VALUES
OF *t*

A quantity that is used as the basis of a judgment is called a "criterion." One such quantity is t, and the following table sets out its "critical values" such that t being greater than the value given leads to one judgment, while its being less leads to another. These critical values depend upon both the number of degrees of freedom for error and the significance level required; each of these quantities can vary by small steps over a wide range, and consequently a full table would be almost impossibly large. However, the critical values vary smoothly and regularly from one case to another, and the table should be large enough for most purposes. Where it is not, interpolation (or "reading between the lines," as someone once called it) is not difficult.

For example, in Chapter 2 there was a need o know the critical value of t for 14 error degrees of freedom and $P = 0.05$. Fairly obviously, it is about 2.14 or 2.15, and this will often be good enough. If more accuracy is required, as well it might be, it may be obtained thus: The values given, i.e., 10, 12, 15, 20, 30, 60, and ∞, when divided into 60 give the quotients 6, 5, 4, 3, 2, 1, and 0 respectively. Further, for any significance level the critical values of t, when plotted against this new scale, give a line that is nearly straight. If the logarithms of the critical values are plotted, the line is virtually completely straight. For example, working with P equal to 0.05, and writing the degrees of freedom as f, the results are as follows.

f	$\dfrac{60}{f}$	*Critical values*	*log (critical values)*
10	6	2.228	0.3479
12	5	2.179	0.3383
15	4	2.131	0.3286
20	3	2.086	0.3197
30	2	2.042	0.3101
60	1	2.000	0.3010
∞	0	1.960	0.2923

For f equal to 14, $\dfrac{60}{f}$ equals 4.29. The value sought therefore lies 0.29 of the way from one line to the other and 0.71 going the other way. Using the critical values themselves, this gives the value required in Chapter 2 as

$$0.71(2.131) + 0.29(2.179) = 2.145$$

This is in fact correct. Using the logarithms gives

$$0.71(0.3286) + 0.29(0.3383) = 0.3314 = \log 2.145$$

which is the same. Where the two differ, the logarithm rule gives the better value. Often there is very little difference, and usually the simpler rule is good enough.

The figures in this appendix that relate to significance levels $P = 0.2$, 0.1, 0.05, 0.01, and 0.001 are taken from Table III of Fisher and Yates, "Statistical Tables for Biological, Agricultural and Medical Research," published by Oliver & Boyd Ltd., Edinburgh, and used by permission of the authors and publishers. Those that relate to the significance levels $P = 0.025$ and 0.005 were calculated by the author from the corresponding entries in Appendix II.

Critical values of the criterion t

Error degrees of freedom	Significance level P						
	0.2	0.1	0.05	0.025	0.01	0.005	0.001
6	1.440	1.943	2.447	2.969	3.707	4.317	5.959
8	1.397	1.860	2.306	2.751	3.355	3.833	5.041
10	1.372	1.812	2.228	2.634	3.169	3.581	4.587
12	1.356	1.782	2.179	2.560	3.055	3.428	4.318
15	1.341	1.753	2.131	2.490	2.947	3.286	4.073
20	1.325	1.725	2.086	2.423	2.845	3.153	3.850
30	1.310	1.697	2.042	2.360	2.750	3.030	3.646
60	1.296	1.671	2.000	2.299	2.660	2.915	3.460
∞ [1]	1.282	1.645	1.960	2.241	2.576	2.807	3.291

[1] ∞ means "infinity," i.e., the error mean square is known with certainty.

APPENDIX II

CRITICAL VALUES OF F

The tables of critical values of the criterion F, which follow, may be interpolated in essentially the same way as those of t. There are two sets of degrees of freedom involved. Those for error can be placed on a better scale by dividing the actual number into 60, as in Appendix I; those for treatments can be similarly divided into 24. For F the improvement brought about by using logarithms is greater than for t.

For most purposes Table V of Fisher and Yates is sufficient, but that of Merrington and Thompson gives more values and more decimal places. It first appeared in *Biometrika*, volume 33, pages 73–88, and has been published separately as "New Statistical Table No. IV" by the Biometrika Trust.

The figures in this appendix that relate to significance levels $P = 0.2$, 0.1, 0.05, 0.01, and 0.001 are taken from Table V of Fisher and Yates, "Statistical Tables for Biological, Agricultural and Medical Research," published by Oliver & Boyd Ltd., Edinburgh, and used by permission of the authors and publishers. Those that relate to the significance levels $P = 0.025$ and 0.005 are taken from Merrington and Thompson's "New Statistical Table No. IV," published in *Biometrika*, volume 33, pages 73–88, and used by permission of Professor E. S. Pearson and the trustees of *Biometrika*.

Critical values of the criterion F

A. *Six degrees of freedom for the error*

Treatment degrees of freedom	Significance level P						
	0.2	0.1	0.05	0.025	0.01	0.005	0.001
1	2.07	3.78	5.99	8.81	13.74	18.64	35.51
2	2.13	3.46	5.14	7.26	10.92	14.54	27.00
3	2.11	3.29	4.76	6.60	9.78	12.92	23.70
4	2.09	3.18	4.53	6.23	9.15	12.03	21.90
5	2.08	3.11	4.39	5.99	8.75	11.46	20.81
6	2.06	3.05	4.28	5.82	8.47	11.07	20.03
8	2.04	2.98	4.15	5.60	8.10	10.57	19.03
12	2.02	2.90	4.00	5.37	7.72	10.03	17.99
24	1.99	2.82	3.84	5.12	7.31	9.47	16.89
∞	1.95	2.72	3.67	4.85	6.88	8.88	15.75

B. *Eight degrees of freedom for the error*

Treatment degrees of freedom	Significance level P						
	0.2	0.1	0.05	0.025	0.01	0.005	0.001
1	1.95	3.46	5.32	7.57	11.26	14.69	25.42
2	1.98	3.11	4.46	6.06	8.65	11.04	18.49
3	1.95	2.92	4.07	5.42	7.59	9.60	15.83
4	1.92	2.81	3.84	5.05	7.01	8.81	14.39
5	1.90	2.73	3.69	4.82	6.63	8.30	13.49
6	1.88	2.67	3.58	4.65	6.37	7.95	12.86
8	1.86	2.59	3.44	4.43	6.03	7.50	12.04
12	1.83	2.50	3.28	4.20	5.67	7.01	11.19
24	1.79	2.40	3.12	3.95	5.28	6.50	10.30
∞	1.74	2.29	2.93	3.67	4.86	5.95	9.34

C. *Ten degrees of freedom for the error*

Treatment degrees of freedom	Significance level P						
	0.2	0.1	0.05	0.025	0.01	0.005	0.001
1	1.88	3.28	4.96	6.94	10.04	12.83	21.04
2	1.90	2.92	4.10	5.46	7.56	9.43	14.91
3	1.86	2.73	3.71	4.83	6.55	8.08	12.55
4	1.83	2.61	3.48	4.47	5.99	7.34	11.28
5	1.80	2.52	3.33	4.24	5.64	6.87	10.48
6	1.78	2.46	3.22	4.07	5.39	6.54	9.92
8	1.75	2.38	3.07	3.85	5.06	6.12	9.20
12	1.72	2.28	2.91	3.62	4.71	5.66	8.45
24	1.67	2.18	2.74	3.37	4.33	5.17	7.64
∞	1.62	2.06	2.54	3.08	3.91	4.64	6.76

D. *Twelve degrees of freedom for the error*

Treatment degrees of freedom	Significance level P						
	0.2	0.1	0.05	0.025	0.01	0.005	0.001
1	1.84	3.18	4.75	6.55	9.33	11.75	18.64
2	1.85	2.81	3.88	5.10	6.93	8.51	12.97
3	1.80	2.61	3.49	4.47	5.95	7.23	10.80
4	1.77	2.48	3.26	4.12	5.41	6.52	9.63
5	1.74	2.39	3.11	3.89	5.06	6.07	8.89
6	1.72	2.33	3.00	3.73	4.82	5.76	8.38
8	1.69	2.24	2.85	3.51	4.50	5.35	7.71
12	1.65	2.15	2.69	3.28	4.16	4.91	7.00
24	1.60	2.04	2.50	3.02	3.78	4.43	6.25
∞	1.54	1.90	2.30	2.72	3.36	3.90	5.42

E. Fifteen degrees of freedom for the error

Treatment degrees of freedom	Significance level P						
	0.2	0.1	0.05	0.025	0.01	0.005	0.001
1	1.80	3.07	4.54	6.20	8.68	10.80	16.59
2	1.79	2.70	3.68	4.77	6.36	7.70	11.34
3	1.75	2.49	3.29	4.15	5.42	6.48	9.34
4	1.71	2.36	3.06	3.80	4.89	5.80	8.25
5	1.68	2.27	2.90	3.58	4.56	5.37	7.57
6	1.66	2.21	2.79	3.41	4.32	5.07	7.09
8	1.62	2.12	2.64	3.20	4.00	4.67	6.47
12	1.58	2.02	2.48	2.96	3.67	4.25	5.81
24	1.53	1.90	2.29	2.70	3.29	3.79	5.10
∞	1.46	1.76	2.07	2.40	2.87	3.26	4.31

F. Twenty degrees of freedom for the error

Treatment degrees of freedom	Significance level P						
	0.2	0.1	0.05	0.025	0.01	0.005	0.001
1	1.76	2.97	4.35	5.87	8.10	9.94	14.82
2	1.75	2.59	3.49	4.46	5.85	6.99	9.95
3	1.70	2.38	3.10	3.86	4.94	5.82	8.10
4	1.65	2.25	2.87	3.51	4.43	5.17	7.10
5	1.62	2.16	2.71	3.29	4.10	4.76	6.46
6	1.60	2.09	2.60	3.13	3.87	4.47	6.02
8	1.56	2.00	2.45	2.91	3.56	4.09	5.44
12	1.51	1.89	2.28	2.68	3.23	3.68	4.82
24	1.45	1.77	2.08	2.41	2.86	3.22	4.15
∞	1.37	1.61	1.84	2.09	2.42	2.69	3.38

G. *Thirty degrees of freedom for the error*

Treatment degrees of freedom	Significance level P						
	0.2	0.1	0.05	0.025	0.01	0.005	0.001
1	1.72	2.88	4.17	5.57	7.56	9.18	13.29
2	1.70	2.49	3.32	4.18	5.39	6.35	8.77
3	1.64	2.28	2.92	3.59	4.51	5.24	7.05
4	1.60	2.14	2.69	3.25	4.02	4.62	6.12
5	1.57	2.05	2.53	3.03	3.70	4.23	5.53
6	1.54	1.98	2.42	2.87	3.47	3.95	5.12
8	1.50	1.88	2.27	2.65	3.17	3.58	4.58
12	1.45	1.77	2.09	2.41	2.84	3.18	4.00
24	1.38	1.64	1.89	2.14	2.47	2.73	3.36
∞	1.28	1.46	1.62	1.79	2.01	2.18	2.59

H. *Sixty degrees of freedom for the error*

Treatment degrees of freedom	Significance level P						
	0.2	0.1	0.05	0.025	0.01	0.005	0.001
1	1.68	2.79	4.00	5.29	7.08	8.49	11.97
2	1.65	2.39	3.15	3.93	4.98	5.80	7.76
3	1.59	2.18	2.76	3.34	4.13	4.73	6.17
4	1.55	2.04	2.52	3.01	3.65	4.14	5.31
5	1.51	1.95	2.37	2.79	3.34	3.76	4.76
6	1.48	1.87	2.25	2.63	3.12	3.49	4.37
8	1.44	1.77	2.10	2.41	2.82	3.13	3.87
12	1.38	1.66	1.92	2.17	2.50	2.74	3.31
24	1.31	1.51	1.70	1.88	2.12	2.29	2.69
∞	1.18	1.29	1.39	1.48	1.60	1.69	1.90

I. Infinite degrees of freedom for the error, i.e., the error is known exactly

Treatment degrees of freedom	Significance level P						
	0.2	0.1	0.05	0.025	0.01	0.005	0.001
1	1.64	2.71	3.84	5.02	6.64	7.88	10.83
2	1.61	2.30	2.99	3.69	4.60	5.30	6.91
3	1.55	2.08	2.60	3.12	3.78	4.28	5.42
4	1.50	1.94	2.37	2.79	3.32	3.72	4.62
5	1.46	1.85	2.21	2.57	3.02	3.35	4.10
6	1.43	1.77	2.09	2.41	2.80	3.09	3.74
8	1.38	1.67	1.94	2.19	2.51	2.74	3.27
12	1.32	1.55	1.75	1.94	2.18	2.36	2.74
24	1.23	1.38	1.52	1.64	1.79	1.90	2.13

INDEX

Where several references are given under a heading, the most important is shown in **boldface** type.

Acton, F. S., 199
Additivity, **54–56,** 69–70, 177
Analysis, of covariance (*see* Covariance, analysis of)
   of variance (*see* Variance, analysis of)
Anderson, R. L., 199
Angles of equal information, 58, 63
Anscombe, F. J., 63
Apple experiments, data of, branch notching, 86
   cover crops, 94
   rootstocks, 24–25
Armitage, P., 199
Association, noncorrelative, 152
   (*See also* Correlation coefficient)
Assumptions, in analysis, of covariance, 176–177
   of variance, 50–57
   in component analysis, 189–190
   hidden, 64–65
Asterisks to mark significance levels, 19

Back transformation, 61–62
Bacon, F., 14
Bailey, N. T. J., 198
Balance, group, 97–98
   supplemented, 90–91
   total, **82–83,** 89
Bancroft, T. A., 199
Bartlett, M. S., 52
Bartlett's Test, 52–53, 177
Blocks, 32, **34–35,** 39, 51, 79, 171, 175–176
   randomized, **35–37,** 111, 131
   analysis of variance for, 36–38
Blood groups, distribution of, 2–3

Carroll, L., 2
Causation, 151–154, 158–160, 162–163, 180–181

Cervantes, M. de, 150
Checks on computations, 36, 72, 74–76, 89, 96, 131–132
Cherry fungicide experiment, data of, 100
χ, 53
Cochran, W. G., 53, 197
Columns, 40–41, 46–48
Communalities, 193–194
Component analysis, 182–196
Computers, electronic, 111, 181
Concurrences, 82–83
Confidence belt, 17, 23
Confidence limits, 17–18, 23, 62
Confounding, 147–148
Correlation coefficient, 150–158, 171, 182
   multiple, 157–158, 194
   partial, 154, 157–158
Covariance, analysis of, 110, **170–177**
   example of, 171–173
   multiple, 173–174
Cox, D. R., 198
Cox, G. M., 197
Criterion, definition of, 7, 201
   Duncan's, 24–25
   F, 19, 201
     tables of, 204–208
   t, 18, 21–22
     relation to *F* criterion, 23
     sequential, 23
     tables of, 202

Darwin, C. R., 150
Data, aberrant, 114–115
   extreme values in, 64–65
   missing data (*see* Plot, missing)
   preliminary examination of, 64
   reasons for analyzing, 4–5
   rejection of, 113–117
Decimal places, number needed, 10, 44, 157, 183, 188–189

Designs, experimental, balanced incomplete blocks, 83–84, 111
    unreduced, 84–85
  complements of, 83
  diminished, 77–78, 102–103
  doubling of, 84
  extension of, 84
  Graeco-Latin square, 40–46
  Latin square, 40–43, 77, 111
    multiple, 47
    tied, 47
  nonorthogonal, 70–104, 109, 173–174
    partitioning with, 124–125
    of type G, 97–104, 125
    of type S, 89–97, 124–126
    of type T, 82–89, 124
  orthogonal, definition of, 35
    four-way, 45
    three-way, 40
    two-way, 34–38, 69
  Youden square, 77
Deviation, definition of, 7
  mean-squared, 15, 19
  standard, 15
  along vector, 185
Deviations, sum of, products of, 150–151
  squared, 8, 14, 33, 68–69
Difference, least significant, 23, 36, 38
Discontinuity, 56–57, 62–63
Duncan, D. B., 24

Eddington, A. S., 64
Effects, linear, 125–126, 127
  systematic, 138
Equations, of constraint, 71–73
  normal, 71
Error, definition of, 7, 14, 32, 69
  homogeneity of, 52–54, 177
  magnitude of, 34, 39, 43, 79, 148
  measurement of, 7, 39, 46–47, 55, 135–137
  standard, 17–18, 52, 108, 163–164, 173
Estimation, 4, 16–18
Ethics, medical, 26
Euler, L., 40
Experimentors, rule of, 4, 6
Experiments, definition of, 4
  designs for (see Designs, experimental)
  factorial, 98
  individuality of, 5
  reasons for, 2, 158–160

Experiments, sensitivity of, 20–21, 26–27
  sequential, 25–29

F test, 19–21, 120
  (See also Criterion; Test)
Factor analysis, 193–194
Factors, definition of, 128
  (See also Partitioning of variation, factorial)
Fawkes, G., 106
Federer, W. T., 198
Figures, significant, 43
Finney, D. J., 198, 199
Fisher, Sir R. A., 1, 197
Freedom, degrees of, definition of, 9
  independence of, 9, 122
  individual, 120–121, 141
  number of, 9, 39, 47, 51, 107, 138, 163

Galton, F., 3, 150
Gin and ministers of religion, 154
Godolphin, S., 2
Goulden, C. H., 197
Grades, subjective, 56
Graeco-Latin squares, 40–46
Grass-cutting experiment, data of, 43, 134
Group-divisible designs (see Designs, experimental, nonorthogonal, of type G)

Haddon, A. C., 3
Hewson, A. D., 26
Hill, A. Bradford, 199
Hoel, P. G., 200
Hogben, L. T., 3
Homogeneity of error (see Error, homogeneity of)
Howeler, J. F., 26
Huxley, Sir J., 3
Hypothesis, generation of, 181
  testing of (see Test)

Insect counts, 59
Interactions, 130–133, 140–148
Interpolation, 201, 203
Iteration, 112, 183, 195–196

Jeffers, J. N. R., 198

Kant, I., 64
Kekulé, F. A., 3
Kempis, Thomas a, 32
Kempthorne, O., 198
Kendall, M. G., 199, 200
Kepler, J., 3

Lamb-grazing experiment, data of, 128
Latin squares (*see* Designs, experimental)
Laws, natural (*see* Relationships, functional)
Least significant difference (*see* Difference, least significant)
Limits of variation (*see* Confidence limits)
Linnaeus, C., 181

Mainland, D., 199
Mather, K., 199, 200
Matrix, correlation, 184, 189, 194
    dispersion, 182, 184, 194
    residuary, 188
    variance-covariance, 184, 189, 194
Mean-squared deviation, 15, 19
Means, adjusted, 73, 88, 96, 103, 171–172, 174
    treatment, 9, 50, 61, 171–174
Mendel, G. J., 24
Milton, J., 68
Missing data (*see* Plot, missing)
Mixed-up plots, 175
Multiple range test, 24–25, 45

Newton, I., 3
Nomination, 21–22, 29, 123
Numbers, manner of writing, 10

Occam, William of, 19
Oscillation, 188

Parameters, definition of, 69
    estimation of, 72, 74–75, 88, 96, 112
Partitioning of variation, 10, 21, 120–138
    factorial, 128–138, 142–147
    polynomial, 125–126
Paterson, D. D., 197
Pea-gibberelic acid experiment, data of, 142

Pea-growth substance experiment, data of, 36
Pear-graft union experiment, data of, 10–11
Percentages, transformation of, 58
Plot, definition of, 32
    missing, 106–117, 137, 175, 177
    mixed-up, 175
    split, 133–138, 147
Plum-size measurements, data of, 155
Poe, E. A., 120
Pope, A., 180
Poppy counts in oats, data of, 53
Population, definition of, 8
Pregnancy toxaemia experiment, data of, 26
Probability levels, 17, 26

Q values (*see* Totals, adjusted treatment)
Quenouille, M. H., 198

Randomization, 35, 41, 50–51, 80, 138
Range, 25, 59
Regression coefficient, 160–167, 180
    curvilinear, 166–167
    partial, 165–166
Relationships, functional, 154, 162–163
Religion, ministers of, and gin, 154
Replication, 51–52, 89–90
    effective, 80, 85, 94, 101, 103–104
Residuals, 55–56, 60, 78, 89, 106, 111–115, 177
Rows, 40–41, 46–48

Sampford, M. R., 199
Sample, 8
    in relation to population, 9
Saunders, H. G., 198
Self-concurrences, 83
Sensitivity, 20–21, 26–27
Sequential experiments 25–29
Shakespeare, W., 140
Significance, 19–20
    levels of, 19–23
        protective, 22, 115
Significant difference, 23, 36, 38
Smallpox, incidence of, among dairymaids, 20

Smith, C. A. B., 200
Snedecor, G. W., 197
Square, Graeco-Latin, 40–46
  Latin (*see* Designs, experimental)
  Youden, 77
Standard deviation, 15
Standard error (*see* Error, standard)
Statistician, role of, 6, 181
Steele, R., 82
Stimulus (*see* Causation; Component analysis)
Subplot, Sub^{2}plot, Sub^{3}plot, etc., 133–138, 147
Sum of squared deviations (*see* Deviations, sum of, squared)
Summation terms, 33, 151
Surveys, 158–160
Swift, J., 170

t test, one-sided, 23–24
  sequential, 26–28
  two-sided, 21–22
  (*See also* Criterion; Test)
Terms, summation, 33, 151
Test, 4, 7, **14**, 19, 21
  Bartlett's, 52–53, 177
  conditional, 120–121, 131, 143–145
  of homogeneity of error, 52–54
  multiple range, 24–25, 45
  of nonadditivity, 56
  of residuals, 113–114
  (*See also* F test; t test)
Tobacco virus experiment, 77
Totals, adjusted treatment, **72,** 87, 94, 101
Transformations, **57–63,** 177, 189, 194

Transformations, angular, 58, 63
  logarithmic, **57,** 59, 63, 155, 189, 194
  square root, 16, 26, **57,** 59, 63
  (*See also* Back transformation)
Treatment, definition of, 32

Validity of experiments (*see* Assumptions)
Variance (*see* Error, measurement of)
  analysis of, 12, 14
    examples of, 15, 38, 44, 61, 74, 87, 88, 95, 102, 107, 113, 127, 129, 130, 136, 143, 144, 145, 158, 165, 172, 173
    logical basis of, 68–69
    paradigms of, 34, 36, 42, 46, 48, 78, 132, 153
Variate, definition of, 33
  dependent, 160
  independent, 160
Variation, coefficient of, 15–16
Vectors, alternative, 191–192
  angle between, 186
  characteristic, 183, 189–190, 196
  deviation along, 185
  guessed, 192–193
  standardization of, 185
Voltaire, F. M. A., 50

Wishart, J., 198

Yates, F., 1, 197, 199
Youden, W. J., 77, 82
Youden square, 77
Yule, G. U., 199